# OUT OF THE DARKNESS

## By Kimberly Grissom

TRILOGY

*Out of the Darkness*
Trilogy Christian Publishers A Wholly Owned Subsidiary of Trinity Broadcasting Network
2442 Michelle Drive Tustin, CA 92780

Rights Department, 2442 Michelle Drive, Tustin, CA 92780.

Trilogy Christian Publishing/TBN and colophon are trademarks of Trinity Broadcasting Network.

Cover design by: Natalee Dunning

For information about special discounts for bulk purchases, please contact Trilogy Christian Publishing.

Trilogy Disclaimer: The views and content expressed in this book are those of the author and may not necessarily reflect the views and doctrine of Trilogy Christian Publishing or the Trinity Broadcasting Network.

Manufactured in the United States of America

10 9 8 7 6 5 4 3 2 1

Library of Congress Cataloging-in-Publication Data is available.
ISBN: 978-1-64773-271-4
E-ISBN: 978-1-64773-272-1

# TABLE OF CONTENTS

# CHAPTER ONE

I watched as the Lamb opened the first of the seven
seals. Then I heard one of the four living creatures say
in a voice like thunder, "Come!" I looked, and there
before me was a white horse! Its rider held a bow, and
he was given a crown, and he rode out as a conqueror
bent on conquest.

*Revelation 6:1-2*

## Friday, August 1, 2025

Olivia awoke with a feeling of impending doom. She was momen-
tarily disoriented as she looked around the room that was not her
childhood bedroom in Florida. After a few seconds, she became
aware of her surroundings. The events of the past year came crashing
down on her as she lay in her bed, delaying the inevitable.

She did not want to get up and face another day without her
father and older sister, Katherine. How much had changed in the
past year! The virus that killed her father and sister also managed
to kill millions of Americans, not to mention millions more across
the globe.

Olivia had heard that it had started in Sierra Leone around
June 2024, when several missionaries from the group Christian
Aid were sent back to their home countries, unknowingly being
infected with a more virulent form of Ebola. The disease spread
quickly to several countries, and within six months, millions had

1

died. The virus was even more deadly than the COVID-19 breakout in 2020. When the Ebola virus broke out, the world had begun returning to normal, people had stopped wearing masks outside, and businesses had returned to ordinary operations. It only took three months before scientists were able to provide a vaccine, but by that time, those that survived ended up having debilitating aftereffects, including blindness and neurological disorders.

Olivia's father was infected early on, and her sister, Katherine, a few months later. Her father was an ER physician in a small hospital in Sarasota, Florida. Her mother was a nurse but stopped working after Katherine was born. Now only Olivia, her mother, and her younger brother, Matt, survived. The doctors said that they were immune to the disease.

All Olivia knew was that the pandemic changed her life forever. She remembered the time before the outbreak and her happy, idyllic childhood. They lived in a 4,200-square-foot home close to the beach, and she went to a private Christian school. Olivia was only fifteen when the outbreak occurred, and her brother Matt was eleven. Their mother, Elizabeth Ahren, felt, after Katherine died, that the best option for them was to pack up and move to their summer home in Blue Ridge, Georgia. She sold the home in Sarasota, the motorboat, and most of their belongings. Elizabeth felt it was important for them to have a fresh start. That was just over two months ago, and Olivia was devastated. Not only did she lose her father and sister, but she had to leave behind all of her friends.

Tomorrow would be her sixteenth birthday, and all the plans she had made would never come to fruition. Since she was twelve years old, she and her sister talked about their sixteenth birthday parties and what they would do. Katherine's birthday was a year before the devastating events, and Olivia was thankful that her sister was able to have the party of her dreams.

"Olivia, are you going to sleep all day?" Elizabeth yelled from the kitchen.

"I'm getting up," Olivia yelled back. "Although I don't know why I have to; it is not like I go to school or have anywhere to go," she grumbled under her breath. She swung her feet out from under the covers and tentatively placed them on the floor. Olivia was still not used to the cold floors of north Georgia. She sat on the side of the bed for a few minutes, looking around. Boy, did she miss her old bedroom! Her mother had hired an interior decorator for her thirteenth birthday to help her redecorate her room. Olivia had meticulously chosen every item, creating a beautiful serene retreat for herself.

As Olivia looked around her current bedroom, tears formed in her eyes. The room was dark and rustic appearing. There were pictures on the wall that the previous owner had purchased. When Olivia's parents bought the cabin, it was furnished. They had not put a lot of effort into changing the décor, as they only spent one to two months a year here. Elizabeth had offered to fix up her room, but Olivia had no desire to do so and was still hoping that this was a temporary situation.

Olivia was just finishing getting dressed when her younger brother, Matt, came running into the room, hastening her, "Hurry up, Olivia! Mom said we can go into town today."

Although Matthew was almost four years younger than her, he was as tall as Olivia, taking after their father, who was six feet two inches. She often saw traces of her father in Matt's expressions and his almost stoic approach to life. She missed his lighthearted personality that seemed to disappear with the death of Katie and their dad.

Olivia perked up at the thought of getting out of the house. She loved going into the small town of Blue Ridge, looking through the shops, and trying samples of the fudge.

"All right, I'm coming. Tell Mom I will be down in five minutes; I just have to brush my teeth and my hair."

At that, Olivia walked into her bathroom and looked into the mirror. She picked up the hairbrush and began brushing her long dark blonde hair. Olivia's hair was always her pride and joy. She never wanted to cut it, and it was down past her waist. Following brushing her hair, she quickly brushed her teeth. She decided she would put a little mascara on and some blush. Olivia looked critically at her face as she applied her makeup. She loved that her eye color was the same as her father's, a pale blue that was fringed with dark eyelashes. Olivia was the only child to get her father's blue eyes; her siblings' eyes matched their mother's hazel color. Her eye color was the only similarity between Olivia and her father; otherwise, she was a younger version of her mother with her small upturned nose, full lips, and high cheekbones. Thinking of her father just made her more homesick, so she turned away from the mirror, ran out of the bathroom, and down the stairs into the kitchen.

"It's about time you got up; breakfast is getting cold," Elizabeth said as she set a plate of pancakes, sausage, and strawberries in front of Olivia. "Hurry up if you want to go to town; I have to work this evening."

Elizabeth went to work at the hospital in Blue Ridge shortly after they moved to Georgia. She had received a life-insurance policy on her husband and money from the sale of the house, but she was afraid it would not last forever.

Olivia hurriedly ate her breakfast, as she was anxious to leave the cabin and actually have contact with other people. When they moved to Georgia, her mother decided that she and Matt would be homeschooled to lessen their chances of being exposed to any other diseases. Olivia felt her mom was just being overprotective since Katie died. She finished out her sophomore year, and Matt finished sixth grade just before they moved to Blue Ridge. The new school year would start in a few weeks, and Olivia was not happy with being homeschooled. She was not worried about the schoolwork, but she was afraid she would miss the socialization with her friends and the after-school activities that she participated in. She used to play volleyball and soccer; now, she did nothing but occasionally FaceTimed her friends in Florida. That had even decreased in the past month, as her friends' lives seemed to have gone on without her. Olivia had not made any friends in Blue Ridge and felt that the outbreak ruined her entire life. She just wished that everything would go back to the way it was.

## Chapter Two

Elizabeth drove their three-year-old GMC Acadia down the mountains into the town of Blue Ridge. It was about a twenty-minute ride from their cabin. Olivia remembered how excited she was when they first bought the cabin five or six years ago and enjoyed vacationing here in the summer. She would never have thought that this would be her permanent home. She missed the palm trees that lined the streets of Sarasota and the beautiful Siesta Key beach that was known for its whitest and softest sand.

Her mom parked at the train depot. When Olivia got out of the Acadia, she was still expecting the hot, humid air of summer in Sarasota. Today, the air had a chill to it, even though it was August 1.

"You kids can wander around: just stay together and meet back here at twelve thirty. We will have lunch together, and then I need to drive us back home to get ready for work."

"Where are you going?" Olivia asked her mom.

"I have some errands to run; I'll see you back here at twelve thirty." With that, Elizabeth gave forty dollars to each of the kids and walked briskly toward Blue Ridge Park.

"Let's get some fudge, Liv," Matt excitedly said as he ran toward The Chocolate Express.

"Wait for me! I am not running there; it is just down the street. Plus, Mom said we need to stick together."

Matt slowed down, and they walked together toward the confectionary shop.

Once they got to the store, they both deeply inhaled the sweet smell of fudge and chocolate. Matt ordered his favorite dark-chocolate peanut-butter cup, and Olivia got a square of Snickers fudge. They both began eating as soon as they left the shop. They wandered around downtown a while, going into several of the antique shops, not purchasing anything. Soon they both tired of shopping, and Olivia suggested that they start walking toward the park. Olivia was looking around, trying to figure out where their mother had gone. It was not like Elizabeth to be secretive.

Olivia just got to Church Street when she saw her mom exit the Blue Ridge Methodist Church. Olivia stopped abruptly, grabbed her brother's arm, and pointed at her mother with her free hand.

"Hey Matt, there is Mom over there. What do you think she was doing in the church on a Friday morning?"

Matt responded, "I don't know, but why don't we go ask her?"

They ran over to their mother, who looked surprisingly guilty as she saw her children.

Matt got to her first and blurted out, "What were you doing in the church?"

Olivia chimed in, "And that is not even *our* church!"

Elizabeth responded, "I just had to ask Pastor Thomas some questions. He was at the hospital the other day visiting a patient, and he invited me to come to their weekly meeting at the church. The meeting is tomorrow evening, and I just wanted to know a little more about what it would entail."

"Why was it such a secret then?" Olivia questioned her mother.

"I really did not mean for it to be a secret; I just did not feel that I needed to explain myself to you two. I thought you would be glad to get a chance to come to town this morning instead of just sitting in the cabin, moping around."

Olivia still felt her mother was hiding something but decided to let it go; instead, she asked, "Well, are you going to the meeting tomorrow, and can I come?"

Elizabeth looked at her, surprised. "You would want to come with me?"

"Sure, what else do I have to do? And Pastor Thomas has a cute son."

Her mother laughingly responded, "I knew you had to have an ulterior motive, but sure. I would love the company."

Matt looked disgusted and stated, "You can count me out; I don't want to go to church once a week, let alone twice. Can we go get lunch now? I'm starving."

"It is not even twelve yet, and we just ate breakfast and chocolate. How can you be hungry?" Olivia asked.

Matt responded by patting his belly, saying, "I'm a growing boy. I need my food."

Elizabeth quickly intervened before Olivia could come back with a sarcastic remark: "How about we go to Blue Jeans Pizza and Pasta Factory? It's a short walk, and that might stimulate your appetite, Liv." Both kids agreed, and they walked several blocks to their favorite pizza place.

After lunch, they wandered around Blue Ridge for a while longer, looking into the stores. Nobody ended up buying anything, but it was fun for Olivia just to be out and be around other people. According to her mom, the virus did not really affect the people of Blue Ridge terribly. Very few were infected, and by the time the virus got around to them, the Aldric pharmaceutical company had developed a vaccine. Olivia wished that Sarasota had not been affected, as several of her friends' families had suffered from the outbreak. The parents of Kylie, her best friend, had died, and she had to go live with her mother's best friend, Sara, and her husband, Mike. They never had children of their own, and Kylie was having a difficult time adjusting, but at least she did not have to leave her hometown. When Olivia would complain about how unhappy she was, Elizabeth would try to help her feel better by telling Olivia that home was not the same since the outbreak, but she could not think of anything being worse than her situation now.

"Mom, can we get some magazines? I would like to know what's going on in the rest of the world," Olivia asked as they were walking toward their SUV. They had spotty cell reception at the cabin, and the internet was not always reliable.

"Sure, we can pick some up outside of the train depot."

Olivia grabbed three gossip magazines, and as soon as they got back to their vehicle and buckled up, Olivia began perusing the first-magazine articles. The first one that caught her eye was "Prodigal Son Marcus Aldric Attempting to Unite the United States and European Nations." The article went on to describe Marcus as the adopted son of John and Mary Aldric, who became heir to the Aldric fortune following his parents' mysterious death when he was sixteen years old.

His parents had owned a large pharmaceutical company and were killed in a car accident when their brakes gave out, and they hit an electrical pole at high speed. The death was ruled accidental, but one reporter felt it was no accident. His name was Phillip Roberts, and he was found dead by apparent suicide six months later. This all happened sixteen years ago, and Marcus was now thirty-two years old.

Aldric Pharmaceuticals was the company that had developed and distributed the vaccine for the Ebola virus. Marcus was the most loved person on the planet at this time, and many praised his philanthropy, as he distributed the vaccine free of charge. According to the article, leaders of several of the European countries, as well as the United States, had died, and the countries were in total chaos. Marcus was attempting to create a centralized government to create order and allow the world economy to return to normal.

Olivia had been totally oblivious as to what had been going on in the rest of the world. She was so focused on her own misery that it did not dawn on her that the entire world was affected by the outbreak.

The article continued to report that China and Russia were resisting the alliance. The reporter expressed concern that if they did not comply, there was a chance that World War III would break out. Olivia read this part out loud to her mother and brother.

Elizabeth reacted by dismissing it, stating, "They have been warning of an impending World War III for the past ten years. I don't think we have anything to worry about."

Olivia hoped her mother was right and decided to finish reading the rest of the article when she got home.

As Elizabeth pulled into the driveway, their neighbors, Susan and Tyler Webber, were outside with their two young children, getting ready to go on a bike ride. The Ahrens all waved to the young family as they exited the SUV.

Tyler jogged over to the family and asked, "How are you guys doing? If there is anything you need, just let us know."

Tyler and Susan were in their early forties. Tyler was dark-haired and dark-eyed, whereas his wife was an ash blonde with pale blue-gray eyes. They were an attractive couple who maintained their slim figures by jogging, biking, or hiking in the nearby woods. They had put off having children until a few years ago, as they both had high-powered jobs in New York. Tyler was a financial advisor, and Susan was a prosecutor for a large law firm. Olivia and her family had not known them prior to the outbreak. The Webbers had moved in approximately six months ago. They had lived in New York and, like Elizabeth, decided to move to an area that was less prone to be exposed to any diseases. Their children had thankfully escaped the virus. Peyton was six and was a blue-eyed little blonde. She was quiet and sweet. Cooper was four and looked like a miniature version of his father. He was into everything and full of energy.

"I appreciate that, Tyler; we are fine for now," Elizabeth responded with a grateful look on her face.

It was upsetting to Olivia that they potentially would need to rely on others. There was a time when her family was the ones who everyone came to for help. The neighbors would come to them for any medical issue, whether small or extreme. Elizabeth was always the one that reached out to assist others, and now they potentially would need help.

"Matt, we are going on a bike ride; we would love for you to join us."

"No, thanks," Matt responded quickly and rushed into the house, slamming the door behind him.

"I hope I did not upset him," Tyler said questioningly.

"He will be fine. I'm not sure what got into him, but I do appreciate you including him. It has been so hard without his dad here," Elizabeth said apologetically.

"Well, let us know if there is anything we can do," Tyler replied as he turned and walked back to his waiting family. The family rode off on their bikes as Olivia was walking into the home.

"What has gotten into Matt? He has never been rude," her mom questioned her.

"Matt misses Dad a lot, and they used to ride bikes together on the weekends. I think he just misses that."

Elizabeth sank onto the couch and put her head in her hands. "I cannot believe I did not think of that. I'm so caught up in my own grief that I forget how difficult this has been for the two of you."

Olivia sat next to her mom and put her arm around her. "It's okay, we understand. This has been hard for all of us. We are just trying to make the best of it. Sometimes it is harder than usual."

"When did you get so smart?" Elizabeth jokingly responded as she turned and hugged her daughter. "I am so glad I have the two of you."

"I feel the same way, Mom. I don't know what Matt and I would have done if you caught the virus too. I was jealous that Kylie was able to stay in Sarasota, but I cannot imagine losing both of my parents."

"It is not unusual to think that everyone else is better off than you when dealing with grief. I am sure that Kylie would give anything to have at least one of her parents back."

Elizabeth got up and walked toward the stairs.

"I need to talk to Matt before I go to work." With that, she ran up the stairs and headed for her son's room.

## CHAPTER THREE

That evening, Olivia warmed up leftover tuna noodle casserole for her and Matt. After dinner, she decided to finish reading the article in the magazine that her mother had bought her earlier in the day. She was fascinated with Marcus Aldric and wanted to know more about him. She turned on her laptop and googled Aldric Pharmaceuticals. She was surprised that she had reception, as she often was unable to get Wi-Fi in their cabin. Many of the articles about Mr. Aldric praised his contribution to ending the Ebola outbreak. There was little about his early life. The Aldrics were a wealthy family who were unable to have children of their own. They went through an international adoption agency and were matched with Marcus shortly after his birth. Marcus' adoptive parents died when he was sixteen, and by the time he was eighteen years old, he was chief executive officer of his family's pharmaceutical company. He was on the Forbes list of the top ten richest individuals in the world five years ago, at the age of twenty-seven. The article described him as a philanthropist who saved the world from further deaths by not only developing the vaccine that slowed the Ebola virus but also doing it free of charge. He went to poor, underserved areas himself and delivered the vaccine.

After a half-an-hour reading of current events, Olivia decided to shut the computer down and go to bed. She was excited about the meeting at the church tomorrow, as she was looking forward to seeing Caleb Monroe again.

The next morning Olivia was awoken by her mother and brother singing "Happy Birthday" to her. They had a tray filled with her favorite breakfast food, chocolate chip pancakes, raspberries, bacon, and chocolate milk with whipped cream on top. This had been her traditional breakfast for as long as she could remember. She smiled and thanked her mom and Matt but was trying to keep the tears at bay. All she could think of was that her father and Katie should be there. It was just so unfair that her life had been turned upside down.

"As soon as you are done eating, why don't we go for a long hike or bike ride?" her mom suggested.

"I'm not really in the mood to commune with nature today, maybe tomorrow. I was hoping to just chill today. Maybe we can go into town early and have dinner before the meeting tonight and walk around a bit?" Olivia asked.

"Sure, that sounds like a great idea. Matt, are you positive you do not want to go?"

Matt responded quickly, "I guess if you are going to throw in dinner, I will have to go. Do I have to stay for the meeting, or can I bring my Nintendo Switch and play some games?"

"Sure, but you need to stay in the church. What about you, Matt? Do you want to go on a walk with me?"

"Okay, but I get to pick the trail we go on," Matt responded.

"All right, let's get moving before it gets too hot. We will see you later, Liv."

Olivia finished her breakfast and laid in bed for a while, thinking how her life would be so different if the virus had not hit the United States. If only her dad and sister were still alive, her life would be perfect. At least she had tonight to look forward to.

Olivia finally dragged herself out of bed and decided to clean her room up. When she heard her mom and Matt come into the cabin, she decided to join them downstairs.

"I'm glad you decided to finally get up so we can give you your present."

"Present? I did not even ask for anything! It didn't even cross my mind that you would be getting me anything this year."

"I know it was not the sixteenth birthday you dreamed of, but it is still special, and do you think I would not get you anything?" her mother asked. Olivia just shrugged her shoulders.

"Well, come outside and see," her mother excitedly responded.

They all walked outside, and in the driveway, Olivia saw a light-blue Volkswagen Cabriolet with a big red bow on it.

"Oh my gosh, is that for me?" Olivia asked in disbelief.

"Of course it is for you; I'm not giving Matt a car. Do you like it?" her mother asked.

"Do I like it? Of course, I love it. This is the car I have always wanted. I cannot believe you got it for me."

"I wanted to make this birthday special. I know how much you have lost and how much I disrupted your life by moving us here. It will not make up for everything, but I was hoping it would help a little."

"Thank you, Mom. I absolutely love it. I love you, and I know this has not been easy for you either. This is the perfect gift. Now I just need my license, and I can drive it."

Olivia had gotten her permit on her fifteenth birthday and was planning on getting her license as soon as she turned sixteen. With everything that happened in the past year, she had not had the opportunity to practice driving and did not feel confident in taking her test at this time.

"We can work on that next week," her mother promised.

Elizabeth handed the keys to Olivia, and she immediately jumped into the driver's seat, placed the key in the ignition, and started the car.

"Mom, get in: I want to drive it down the street."

"How about you drive it tonight to dinner and the meeting? For now, you can figure out where everything is."

Olivia agreed and immediately turned the radio to her favorite station and examined the car from top to bottom.

After that, the day seemed to drag. Olivia was looking forward to the meeting tonight and was excited to see Caleb again. She had met him shortly after they moved full-time to Blue Ridge. She and her mother had gone into town and ran into Pastor Thomas and Caleb while sitting in Blue Ridge Park, having a cup of coffee. The Monroes had been walking past when the pastor stopped and introduced himself. He asked if they were new to the town, and Elizabeth had shared the events of the past few months with them. The pastor's wife had also succumbed to Ebola early on and was one of the few to die in Blue Ridge. She had been visiting her sister in Western New York when she was exposed. She became sick while she was still at her sister's and never returned to Blue Ridge. It was fortunate that she did not expose her husband and son, but they were unable to say their goodbyes to her.

Olivia was immediately drawn to Caleb, as they both had lost a parent. It did not hurt that he was also extremely cute. Olivia always liked boys with dark hair and blue eyes, and Caleb had both. His eyes were the clear blue that was the color of the sky on a clear day. He was also tall, around six feet, and angular, which made him more appealing as Olivia was just a tad over five feet eight inches. Just thinking of Caleb made Olivia smile, and she could not wait to see him again.

Finally, it came time for the Ahrens to leave for town. Olivia had spent the previous hour getting ready, making sure her hair and makeup were perfect. It took her thirty minutes to pick out her outfit, and she finally decided on a pair of black skinny jeans, a light-blue sweater, and a pair of blue Converses. She gave herself one last inspection and then joined her mom and Matt, who were already waiting for Olivia outside her new car.

"What took you so long? We have been waiting for ten minutes for you," Matt asked in exasperation.

"You are exaggerating, you guys just got out here, and unlike you, I care about how I look," Olivia responded.

"Okay, both of you, stop arguing, and let's have a good evening. Matt, be nice to your sister at least on her birthday."

"All right, I will try, but it will be difficult," Matt said sarcastically.

Elizabeth asked Olivia, "Do you have your permit with you?"

"Yes, of course. I cannot wait to drive this thing."

"Just don't kill us," Matt said jokingly as he climbed into the back.

Her mom had made reservations at Olivia's favorite restaurant in town. When they were seated, Olivia ordered a diet Coke and shrimp tempura as an appetizer and scallops and risotto as her main dish. Matt got his usual half-pound beef burger. It did not matter where they ate—Matt would get a burger. Her mom ordered a Caesar salad with shrimp.

Dinner was delicious, and they were all comfortably stuffed by the time the waiter cleared away their plates.

Elizabeth and Olivia ordered a coffee, and while they were waiting, the waiters and waitresses came clapping up to the table singing "Happy Birthday," and their waiter was carrying a large piece of chocolate cake with a candle in the middle.

The waiter set the dessert in front of Olivia and quickly disappeared. Olivia gave her mother a look that said, "I'm going to kill you later," and blew out the candle.

"Did you make a wish?" her mother asked.

"Yes, that I never have to go through that embarrassment again."

Matthew laughed and asked if he could have her cake. Olivia pushed it over to him, as she was full from dinner and could not eat another bite.

Their coffees came, and the three of them walked out onto the patio where live music was playing.

They sat for a while and listened to the band and then decided to walk to the church, as it was 6:45 p.m. and the meeting was scheduled for 7:00 p.m.

They arrived just before seven, and Pastor Thomas was at the door to greet them: "Come in; I'm so glad you were able to make it. We are in the sanctuary. If you just follow me, I will introduce you to the other members."

When they walked into the main part of the church, Olivia was surprised to see how many people from the town were at the meeting. There had to be at least forty people present, and although some looked familiar, she did not know any of them by name.

Pastor Thomas walked up to the pulpit and began speaking, "Good evening, folks. I would like to take a moment to introduce new members of our group." He gestured for Elizabeth, Olivia, and Matt to come up to the stage. "This is Elizabeth Ahren, her daughter Olivia, and her son Matthew. They have recently moved to Blue Ridge full-time from Florida. Some of you may recognize Elizabeth as a nurse at the hospital. I hope you all make them feel welcome. If you could all go around the room and say a few words about yourselves, that would be great."

A gentleman in the front raised his hand, stating, "I will start things off. My name is Mark Downing, and this is my wife, Karen. We have two children who are home with the babysitter tonight. We grew up in Blue Ridge, and we wouldn't live anywhere else. We both work at Ingles Market and are glad to have you join our group."

Elizabeth came down from the stage and shook Mark and Karen's hands and thanked them for the warm greeting. Olivia felt awkward standing on the stage, so she nudged Matt, and they both surreptitiously walked off the stage and wandered to the back of the sanctuary, where Olivia noticed some of the younger crowd was hanging out. The other members of the church were introducing themselves, but Olivia ignored this as she went up to a face she recognized in the group of six teenagers.

"Hey, Caleb, how are you doing?"

"I didn't know you would be here tonight, Olivia; it's good seeing you again."

"Thanks! Mom mentioned this meeting yesterday, and I thought it would be fun to get out of the cabin and see other people for a change."

"I get that; since the virus, we have all been pretty isolated. This meeting at least lets us get together once a week to socialize."

Caleb then began introducing Olivia and Matt to the other teenagers in the group. He first gestured to the girl on his right, "This is Clara; her parents own one of the shops downtown."

Clara was dark-skinned, with almost black eyes and curly black hair. When she spoke, her voice had a slight southern accent, "It is nice to meet you, Olivia and Matt."

Caleb went on to introduce the pair to the rest of the group. There was Martha, who liked to be called Marty, Daniel, and Seth and Emma, who were brother and sister. They all greeted Olivia and Matt warmly. As soon as the introductions were over, Emma spoke up and asked Olivia and Matt to tell them what brought their family to Blue Ridge. Olivia told the abridged story of how their life was upended with the virus and how they ended up in Blue Ridge full-time. The group appeared genuinely sympathetic to their plight.

When Olivia was done telling her story, Clara gave Olivia a hug and said, "I'm glad you joined our group. We never have anyone new move here. We get lots of tourists, but the locals have all been here since the town was created."

Olivia returned Clara's warm smile. "It was not like that in Sarasota at all. There were always people moving there and also moving out. I went to a small private school, but every year it seemed that there were new faces."

"I guess both towns have their advantages," Emma added. "I like that I know everyone in school, but Clara's right: it's nice to have new families move in."

Olivia immediately felt a connection to the group. They all welcomed her with open arms, and she sensed a real sincerity about them. As much as Olivia loved living in Sarasota, she did not always feel her friends were genuine, and they often talked behind each other's backs. Olivia, at times, found herself drawn into this and would gossip about her friends, knowing that it was wrong.

The group of teens stood around for a few more minutes talking and getting to know each other when Pastor Thomas announced that the meeting was beginning and asked everyone to take a seat. Matt went to the back of the church and got out his handheld gaming device. Olivia sat more toward the middle of the church, a few rows behind the adults and between Caleb and Clara.

Pastor Thomas started out by welcoming everyone to the meeting, "I'm so glad you were all able to make it tonight. For those that are joining us for the first time: we started meeting a few weeks ago to explore and delve into the book of Revelation. We have discussed chapters one through four, and starting today, we are going to dive into the actual events that will begin the final seven years of tribulation. The events that have been happening over the past year have led us to believe that we are nearing this time. I feel that it is important that we reach out to as many people as possible to prepare them for the times to come. Churches today have become complacent." Pastor Thomas looked around the church with a somber expression. "Bible prophecy is not given to us to scare us but prepare us. It is up to us as Christians to try and save as many people as possible before the end comes.

"Over the next couple of weeks, I plan to discuss the timetable of the seven-year tribulation by starting with the seven seal judgments. Many Christians do not like to read about or discuss this part of the Bible. It can be very frightening to some, but know that as long as you believe in Jesus, you will not need to be afraid."

Olivia was surprised by what Pastor Thomas was saying. She had no idea what this meeting was about but never in her wildest dreams would anticipate it was about the end of the world. She looked at her mother, who sat a few rows up from her, but her mother stared straight ahead, and Olivia could not see her face. She wondered if her mother knew what Pastor Thomas was planning to discuss or if she was just as surprised as Olivia was.

Pastor Thomas continued on, "Once the Antichrist makes his covenant with Israel and other nations, it will begin. I feel that this is going to happen within the next few months, and it is important that we are prepared." Pastor Thomas then took his well-worn Bible and began reading from Revelation.

Olivia had a difficult time following what was being read, as the terminology was quite new to her. Olivia went to a Christian school, and when she lived in Sarasota, she and her parents went to church almost every Sunday, but she had not read much of Revelation. Olivia always thought of the book as telling about what could happen far into the future. She never imagined that it would play out in her lifetime. Olivia still was not convinced that they were getting close to the "end of time" and felt maybe the pastor and other members of the church were just overreacting.

Pastor Thomas finished reading and put the Bible down.

"I know this is scary to some, but it is vital that we get the Word out and ensure that everyone we know and love is prepared for what comes next."

A gentleman in the second row raised his hand and asked, "Pastor Tom, what is coming next? I know all about the seven seals, trumpets, and all that other stuff John talked about in Revelation, but break it down for us! What is going to happen first, and what do we need to do to prepare?"

"That is a great question, Bart. The book of Revelation does lay out God's plans quite clearly, but much of it is symbolic and not easy for everyone to understand. It is important that we use this time to go through the book and identify the timeline for the upcoming seven years."

Pastor Thomas, at this point, went offstage and came back, wheeling in a whiteboard. On it was written:

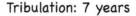

Tribulation: 7 years

Seal Judgments

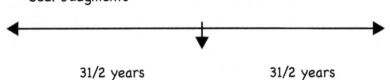

31/2 years               31/2 years

The Seal Judgments (Revelation 6)

First seal: white horse, Antichrist
Second seal: red horse, warfare
Third seal: black horse, world famine
Fourth seal: pale horse, death to 1/4 of the earth
Fifth seal: martyrdom
Sixth seal: physical disturbances (earthquake, sun
    blacked out, etc.)
Seventh seal: heaven is quiet; Church is raptured.

Pastor Thomas went on to explain that there were seven seals that held closed a scroll in heaven. As each seal was broken, there would be a new judgment that would be released on the earth. He explained that the seven years would begin with Jesus opening the first seal, which would release the Antichrist on the earth. Pastor Thomas stated, "And I saw, and behold a white horse: and he that sat on him had a bow; and a crown was given unto him: and he went forth conquering, and to conquer."[1]

Olivia often heard stories about the Antichrist and even watched a few movies that centered on him, but she looked at this as more fiction than real life.

Pastor Thomas went on to say, "I know many of you have questions as to what this means and how it will affect us. First, I don't know who the Antichrist is, but I am sure he will reveal himself in the next few weeks or months. What I do know is that he will claim that his goal is to bring peace to the world, but as we know, that is not at all what he has planned."

Olivia noted that several of the members of the church were whispering to themselves, and many looked concerned. Several raised their hands and began asking questions.

The teenagers all just sat there with shocked looks on their faces. Olivia leaned into Caleb and asked, "Were you aware of all of this?"

"Yes, my dad has talked about it, but I am not sure how much to believe or if it really will happen. For years, different religious leaders have said the end is near, but it has never panned out. I don't know how I feel. On the one hand, I am scared of the world ending. I would like to have a chance to go to college, get married, have kids, but on the other hand, the way the world is going, I am okay with this being it."

Olivia nodded in agreement. "I feel the same way. This past year has been so horrible, I would like to see my sister and dad again, and I can't imagine ever going through that pain again. I also had plans for the future and was looking forward to college."

"Maybe we are getting all upset over nothing; I guess only time will tell. In the meantime, we can only live our lives the best we can," Caleb replied.

Olivia sat and listened for a while, but eventually, she began tuning out both Pastor Thomas and the other members, thinking to herself, *I am not going to get all worked up about this. It's probably never going to happen.*

When the meeting was over, the members dispersed into small groups. Marty left right after the meeting with her parents. Olivia and the rest of the teenagers went to the back of the church to talk among themselves.

Daniel thought that the whole concept was ridiculous, but Clara was convinced that Pastor Thomas was on target with everything he said, and she was going to be prepared.

Olivia questioned her, "What do you mean 'be prepared'? What does that entail?"

Clara responded, "Well, I plan to research everything I can about what was written in Revelation about the Antichrist, as well as what to expect in the last days. Also, Pastor Thomas indicated that it is our responsibility to educate others on Jesus and minister to them."

"How will you do that? I'm not sure I feel comfortable ministering to other people when I don't even know what I am talking about," Olivia responded.

Emma shook her head, stating, "I agree. I do not feel that I am the right person to tell others what they should and should not believe."

Caleb answered with, "I know that I have an advantage, as I grew up a minister's son, but I feel that anyone of us should be able to speak about Jesus and tell others that in order to get into heaven, you have to believe in Him. I don't think my dad wants you all going out and preaching; just tell those that you know and love about Jesus whenever you get a chance."

Seth had been quiet throughout the discussion but finally added, "I think Caleb is right. We have all gone to church since we were little, and I feel that we owe it to our family and friends to spread the word. I have some family members that I really worry about, especially my mom. Since she and Dad split up, she has stopped coming to church. I want her to go to heaven with me, and I will do whatever I can to make sure she does."

Olivia thought about it for a minute and stated, "Well, I guess when you put it like that, it shouldn't be too hard. It will not hurt to try."

Emma and Clara both nodded in agreement.

Daniel still looked skeptical and countered, "Well, I still feel this is all a bunch of hogwash and don't plan on changing anything I'm doing."

Caleb looked sadly at Daniel, replying, "We all have to do what we feel is right, Daniel. I hope you change your mind in the future."

Just then, Elizabeth came up to the group, interrupting them, "Come on, kids, we have to get home. You will get to see everyone tomorrow at the 9:00 a.m. service."

"Before you go, how about we all exchange numbers so if we want to talk, we can call each other?" Clara suggested. They all agreed it was a good idea and took a few minutes to put each other's numbers into their phones.

Once they were finished, Olivia and Matt said their goodbyes and walked out to the Volkswagen. Olivia still could not believe this was her car. She unlocked the doors and slid into the driver's seat.

"I've got to say, Mom: this feels really good."

Elizabeth smiled and said, "I'm happy that you had a good birthday."

Olivia smiled back, assuring her, "I really did, but I have to say: Pastor Thomas's talk of the end of times kind of put a damper on things."

Elizabeth nodded and asked, "Well, what do you think?"

"I'm honestly not sure, Mom," Olivia responded. "I'm scared. Whenever you see movies about the Antichrist, they are pretty much horror flicks. I don't know enough about the Bible to really know what to think."

"That is really a perceptive answer, Olivia. I agree. I know we have gone to church our whole lives, but rarely did the pastors discuss Revelation and the end of the world; they pretty much just glossed over it. I hope by going to these meetings, we will be able to understand it better and get the answers we need."

Elizabeth turned to the back seat where Matt was sitting and asked, "What are your thoughts? You have been pretty quiet."

"I have no clue. I didn't pay attention. I just heard a bunch of doom-and-gloom stories, and I pretty much tuned everything out. I did make it to level five of my game, though."

Elizabeth just shook her head and sighed. "Well, we won't worry about it tonight. Let's listen to some music," and with that, she turned the radio on. On the ride home, they were all silent, caught up in their own thoughts.

# Chapter Four

The next day was Sunday, and Elizabeth woke Olivia and Matt up early to get ready for church. Olivia took her time getting ready, excited to see Caleb again. They did not usually go to Pastor Thomas's church, but Elizabeth had decided last night to start going there since they would be meeting every Saturday night with the other members.

Once Olivia was done showering, she applied special conditioner into her hair to keep it soft and shiny. She then applied a light coat of makeup, making sure she highlighted her blue eyes. She spent the majority of the time trying to decide what to wear. It had been a while since she had gone clothes shopping. She thought she would suggest to her mother the two of them go shopping next weekend. She really missed the mall at home; it had every store imaginable to choose from. She finally settled on a pale blue romper that was sleeveless. She added a cropped white sweater to the outfit, as, in her experience, churches were always cold. As soon as Olivia was done, she ran downstairs to the kitchen, where her mother was busy fixing breakfast.

"Well, don't you look nice? Do you want some yogurt and fruit, or I can make you something more substantial if you want?"

"No, thanks. Yogurt and fruit are fine. Is Matt almost ready?"

"I woke him up, and he grumbled at me. I'll go get him moving. We need to leave in fifteen minutes."

While Elizabeth ran upstairs, Olivia grabbed a yogurt from the fridge, spooned some granola on top, and added strawberries that her mother had prepared.

Pretty soon, Matt and their mother came walking down the stairs. Elizabeth popped a bagel in the toaster and got the cream cheese out of the refrigerator.

Matt complained, "Why do we have to go to church? We were there just yesterday, doesn't that count?"

Elizabeth just glared at him and continued preparing him something to eat. As soon as his bagel was ready, she slid it over to him and said, "Hurry up and eat: we will be leaving in a minute."

As soon as Matt was finished with his bagel, Elizabeth grabbed her purse and keys and said, "Let's go."

They arrived at the church five minutes before nine. Olivia looked around to see if she could see Caleb and within seconds found him sitting up front next to Emma, Seth, and Clara. She turned to her mother and asked if she could sit with them. Her mother agreed. Olivia quickly moved up front and slid into the pew next to Clara. She whispered, "Hey, guys."

Clara turned and smiled at Olivia, greeting her, "I'm so glad you're here. I love your outfit." Caleb and Emma both smiled and said hi. Seth gave her a little wave.

After the church service, Olivia stood and talked with the group for a while. She asked Caleb where Daniel was.

"He doesn't always come to church, only when his family makes him come."

"Oh, I just figured you all came to church every week since he was at the meeting."

"Emma, Seth, Clara, and Marty generally come every week, but Daniel rarely does. Marty is here, but she sat with her family today. Her mother has not been well since she had Ebola and has had some lingering effects."

"I must have missed her. I'm sorry to hear about her mother, but at least she still has her. My friend Kylie lost both her parents to the virus. It is hard enough losing one parent."

"I know my dad, and I have had a hard time since Mom died. We know she is in a better place, but that does not take away that we miss her."

Olivia nodded her head in agreement. She quickly changed the subject and asked Caleb, Seth, Emma, and Clara about school. Emma said she was going to be a senior in Fannin County High School and would be going for half a day. The rest was online. Both Caleb and Clara were homeschooled like Olivia. All three of them were going to be juniors this year. Seth was a sophomore and was also going to school in person.

Olivia found she had a lot in common with the other teenagers and was looking forward to getting to know them better. She asked, "Do you guys hang out any other times because I would love to join you? It has been so boring since we moved here."

Clara linked her arm in hers, "Occasionally, we meet downtown and get coffee or a bite of pizza. In fact, we were talking about getting together tomorrow evening for tacos at Las 2 Huastecas. They are closed on Sundays, or we would go today."

"That sounds great; let me just ask my mom. She works at the hospital two nights a week, so I am not sure she works tomorrow. I don't have my license yet, so I can't drive myself."

Caleb spoke up, "I can pick you up. You do not live far from me."

"That would be great, but I still have to ask my mom's permission. What time are you thinking?"

"I can pick you up around five thirty, and we can all meet around six," Caleb answered.

"Let me go ask my mom, and I will be right back."

Olivia walked over to her mother, who was speaking with a woman that she did not recognize.

"Oh hey, Olivia, this is Trish. I work with her at the hospital. She is a nurse on the same floor I work."

"Nice to meet you, Olivia. Your mother talks about you and your brother a lot. It is nice to finally put a face to the name."

"Nice to meet you too. Mom, the other kids were planning on going to get tacos tomorrow evening. Caleb offered to pick me up and take me. I was wondering if I could go."

"Sure, I'm off tomorrow, so Matt would not be home alone. Although you could ask him to go with you," her mom replied.

"I guess I could. Where is he? I have not seen him since the service started."

"He found some boys his age, and they went off talking about some video game. I think he is outside. Would you go find him, as we are leaving in a minute?"

"Okay. Let me go say goodbye to my friends and let them know I can go tomorrow, and then I will look for him."

Olivia walked back over to Caleb and the girls.

"Good news, I can go tomorrow. Do you need my address, Caleb?"

"No, Dad pointed out your cabin a few weeks ago when we drove by. I'll pick you up around five thirty. I'll let you know if I'm running late."

"Sounds good. I will see you all tomorrow. I have to go find my brother, and then we are leaving."

The group all said goodbye, and Olivia walked outside. She immediately saw her brother sitting on a bench outside the church talking to another boy. They both had their phones out, and it looked like they were playing a game.

"Hey, Matt, are you ready to go? Mom sent me out to look for you."

"Yeah, I'm ready. See you later, Mark. Call me later, and we can play Mario Kart."

Mark said his goodbyes and promised to call after lunch just as Elizabeth walked out of the church.

# CHAPTER FIVE

When Olivia woke up on Monday, she did not have the same feeling of gloom that had surrounded her since their move to Blue Ridge. She was actually excited for the day and jumped right out of bed. After completing her morning ritual, she ran downstairs, surprised at how quiet it was.

Olivia yelled out, "Mom, where are you?"

There was no answer. She ran back upstairs and looked in both her mom's and Matt's rooms. Neither of them was there. *That's weird*, Olivia thought to herself. It was unusual that her mom and Matt would leave the house without telling her. She went back downstairs and decided to get something to eat. She tried calling her mom on her cell phone, but it went straight to voice mail. She next tried Matt, and the same thing happened. She was starting to get worried when the front door opened, and her mom and Matt came laughing inside.

Matt was saying something about how he was the champion.

Her mom responded jokingly, "I let you win."

Olivia interrupted their banter, "Where have you, guys, been? I was starting to worry. I thought maybe you were raptured up to heaven and left me behind." Olivia said this in jest, but then she started to think about what Pastor Thomas had said two nights ago and thought, *What if that did happen?* She could not imagine being left totally alone. As hard as it was to lose her sister and father, she could not envision a life without her mother.

"We just went for a bike ride, sleepyhead. You were sound asleep, so Matt and I decided to enjoy the beautiful morning."

"Maybe next time, leave me a note. What if you were kidnapped? How soon before I should call the police and tell them my mother is missing?"

"Well, I think the usual procedure is twenty-four hours when it is an adult. You would be better off telling them Matt was missing; they may take that report."

"Well, since you have not been kidnapped, how about making me some breakfast? I worked up an appetite looking for you."

"I vote for eggs and bacon if you are making breakfast," Matt interjected.

"All right, if you two insist. Olivia, do you have any special requests?"

"No, bacon and eggs sounds good. You could throw in some hash browns, too, though."

After breakfast, Olivia attempted to FaceTime her friend Kylie. There was no answer. She was excited to tell her about the meeting on Saturday and her plans for the evening. It had been so long since she had looked forward to anything.

By the time evening came, Olivia was quite keyed up. She had changed her outfit at least five times.

She yelled downstairs, "Mom, can you come up here and give me your opinion on what I should wear?"

Elizabeth came into her room and gasped, "It looks like a hurricane came through here! I hope you plan on cleaning up this mess before you go." Olivia had clothes strewn everywhere in her room.

"I will, I promise. What do you think of this outfit?"

Olivia had decided upon a pair of linen-colored high-waisted belted pants with a white sleeveless cropped halter top and white Converse sneakers.

Elizabeth cocked her head to the side and said, "Very cute."

"You don't think it looks like I'm trying too hard, do you?"

"Not at all. It's the perfect outfit for a casual evening out with friends. Now, clean up this mess! Caleb will be here in about half an hour, and I would like this room to be back to normal somewhat."

"Thanks, Mom. I appreciate your help," and with that, Olivia began hanging up the clothes she had thrown haphazardly around her room.

Caleb arrived at the Ahrens right on time. Olivia was waiting for him nervously in the kitchen. She jumped a little when the doorbell rang.

She yelled out, "I got it!" She ran to the door and pulled it open. "Hey, Caleb. Thanks for picking me up."

"No problem. Are you ready to go?"

Just as they were getting ready to leave, Elizabeth showed up at the door.

"Hello, Caleb. It is so nice of you to drive Olivia to town. She has been looking forward to it all day."

Olivia silently groaned at this.

"What time do you think you will have her back home?"

"We should not be home any later than eight. We are just getting tacos and maybe walking around the town for a bit."

"Okay. Olivia, call me if you are going to be later than eight. Otherwise, you guys have a good time."

They both yelled out thanks as they were walking out to Caleb's car. He had an older silver Ford Edge.

Olivia jumped in the front seat and buckled up, suddenly feeling nervous.

She and Caleb made small talk on the drive into town. Caleb talked about growing up in Blue Ridge and described his life before the virus outbreak. He had turned sixteen three months ago and had a low-key party with just his closest friends. Caleb discussed his plans for the upcoming school year.

"Even though I am not going to be going to school in person, I'm still on the football team. We have been practicing all summer. You will have to come to the games. It's a lot of fun, and it's a big Friday night out for the whole town."

"That sounds like fun. I used to play soccer and volleyball at my old school. Maybe I can join the teams here, although I am not sure how my mom would feel about that. She has been pretty overprotective since my dad and sister died. I'm surprised she is even letting me out tonight. It probably does not hurt that your father is a pastor in town."

Caleb looked over at her, "Well, I'm glad she did. I was hoping when we met when you first moved here that I would see you again. I had kind of given up hope and was happy to see you walk into the church Saturday night."

Olivia's heart started beating faster. She did not know what to say, so she just responded with, "Really? I was hoping to see you again too."

Thank goodness they pulled up to the restaurant before she said anything that might embarrass herself.

After they parked, they walked up to the restaurant, and Marty and Daniel were waiting outside. Shortly thereafter, Clara, Seth, and Emma showed up.

The group avoided talking about the meeting the other night and focused on discussing the upcoming school year. Like Emma, Daniel was a senior and was looking forward to going away to college next year.

"I cannot wait to get out of this town. I'm hoping to get into Georgia Institute of Technology in Atlanta."

"That's cool. What do you plan on studying?" Olivia asked.

"I am thinking electrical engineering but have not fully committed to this yet."

"What about you, Emma? What do you plan on doing after you graduate?" Olivia questioned.

"I plan on going to Wesleyan College for nursing. Our older sister went there, and she is a nurse now. That is all I ever wanted to do since I was a kid."

"That is so good to know what you want to do and have a plan for the future. My mom's a nurse, and I never thought I would want to do that. My father was a doctor, and I had plans to follow in his footsteps until this virus. Now I do not know what I want to do. After listening to Pastor Thomas, I'm thinking, why even bother if the world is going to end? I might as well have fun while it lasts," Olivia half-jokingly replied.

Daniel chuckled at this comment, "I do not believe any of it is going to pan out, but I agree we should have fun while we can."

After dinner, the group walked around downtown, looking in stores and making small talk. When Olivia noticed it was almost 7:30 p.m., she tugged on Caleb's arm and reminded him that they should probably get going, as she told her mom she would be home by 8:00 p.m. The rest agreed that they needed to get home also. They all said their goodbyes, and Caleb and Olivia walked off to his car.

Once Olivia was back alone with Caleb, she felt shy and nervous again. She never really hung out with a guy alone. When she lived in Sarasota, she would go out with her friends, which included boys, but they were always in a group.

"Did you have a good time tonight?" Caleb asked.

"Yeah, I had a great time. Your friends are really nice. They are definitely different than my friends back in Sarasota."

Caleb looked at her with raised eyebrows. "Really? How is that?"

"It's hard to describe, but the kids here seem more genuine and seem to really care about each other. Whereas in Sarasota, I feel like everything is always a competition: who has the best clothes, most money, and biggest house. You know what I mean."

"I get what you are saying, but it has never been like that here. All of my friends have always been supportive. We could care less about how much your father or mother makes. I personally care how you treat me and others."

"See, that is what I mean. I am not used to that. It's nice to know that you have friends that will have your back when you need them. I feel like I am drifting away from my friends in Sarasota. I used to be so close to my friend Kylie, now we barely talk. I'm sure she is having a hard time adjusting without her parents, but at least she did not have to change schools or her friends."

"Kylie may be feeling that you are the lucky one, as you still have your mom. It is hard to know what someone else is going through. You may want to talk with her about it and let her know you feel that you are drifting apart."

"That is a great idea. I will call her tomorrow and see if I can find out what is going on with her. You know, Caleb Monroe, you give good advice."

"Why, thank you. That will be a dollar."

Olivia smiled warmly at Caleb. "Thanks for including me tonight. I really enjoyed myself. It was nice to forget for a while all the crap that happened this past year."

"Well, I am glad you were able to come. We try to get together at least once a week outside of church."

Caleb pulled into her driveway, turned the car off, and walked her to the door.

They said their goodbyes, and before he left, Caleb pulled her into a hug and said, "I know that you did not want to leave Sarasota, but I'm glad you moved here." He quickly pulled away and waved goodbye as he got into his car.

Olivia just stood and looked at him as he drove off. When she got into the house, she locked the door behind her and heard her mother call out, "Is that you, Livy?"

"Yes, Mom, I'm home."

"Come into the living room and tell me all about your night."

Olivia called back, "Let me go upstairs and change into something more comfortable, and I will give you all the details." And with that, Olivia ran upstairs, smiling the entire way.

# CHAPTER SIX

The next day Olivia reached out to Kylie again. This time she picked up right away.

"I'm so glad you called, Olivia. I meant to call you back the other day, but I have been so busy I totally forgot about it."

"That's okay. I was just wondering how you are doing. Is everything going all right with Sara and Mike?"

"It's okay. They try really hard, but nothing replaces your parents. They have been talking about moving, though. I have been so stressed out. Sara wants to move back to her hometown in New York. It is apparently Hicksville, but she is worried that the virus will return or that there is going to be World War III."

"What about Mike/ Does he want to move too?"

"He will do whatever Sara wants. I am afraid it is going to happen, and I can't do anything about it. It's bad enough that I lost my parents. Now I will lose my friends and my home."

After the virus, Mike and Sara moved into Kylie's parents' home so as to not disrupt her life any more than they had to.

Olivia could totally sympathize with Kylie. "Have you tried talking with them? Let them know how devastating this would be to your life."

"I have tried, but Sara keeps saying she is trying to protect me. I only have two years until I am eighteen, and then I can do whatever I want. I just wish they would hold off on making any decisions until then."

"What can I do to help?"

Kylie sighed. "I don't think there is anything you can do unless you have a time machine that can take us back a year and change the outcome."

"I wish. There are many times I have prayed that this is just a bad dream and that when I wake up, everything is back to normal."

Kylie nodded and said, "Well, I need to get going. I'm supposed to meet Rachel and Lisa at the mall. We are going back to school clothes shopping."

"What, Mike and Sara are letting you go back to school?"

"They haven't decided yet, but they are leaning more toward letting me, as there have been no new virus outbreaks in four months."

"Lucky. I am still relegated to homeschooling, but I have made some friends here. We actually hung out last night."

Kylie responded absently, "That's great. Look, I have to go. Rachel keeps texting me. Let's talk next week."

"Okay. Give me a call when you're free." Olivia hung up with a feeling of sadness. She had a feeling Kylie would not call her back. Looking back at their friendship, she saw that it was mostly one-sided. Kylie often had some sort of drama going on in her life and would expect Olivia to drop everything to be there for her, but Kylie rarely reciprocated and usually did not like to hear about other people's difficulties or their successes.

Olivia was glad that she had found friends in Blue Ridge that actually might be supportive in good times and bad.

Three days later, Olivia was home watching TV. Her mother was at work, and Matt was upstairs playing video games on his PC. She was laying on the couch, watching one of her favorite reality shows, when it was interrupted with breaking news. The newscaster, a middle-aged man named Michael, came on the screen stating that there had been developments in the European Union. He went on to state that leaders from around the world had been meeting behind closed doors to discuss coming together as a world government to help with the recovery from the devastation caused by the Ebola breakout. Michael went on to say that the international council was led by Marcus Aldric as a representative for the United States. They determined that in order to improve the economies that were destroyed by the outbreak, the world needed to come together. They were eliminating all border controls between members. Michael reported that this would allow for easy trade between countries, which would benefit all countries in eliminating tariffs and duties. It would also allow for the practitioners of all services, including physicians, to operate in all countries. Marcus Aldric released a statement to the press, reporting that the expanded European Union would benefit all countries in environmental protection, research, and development and reduce prices of all services. There would be global laws that would go into effect, but each state would ultimately enforce the laws. Mr. Aldric also reported that representatives from Israel and Palestine were discussing coming to a peace agreement and were willing to negotiate a shared agreement for Jerusalem and the Temple Mount. He felt this was a complete success and announced that several countries had agreed to join the European Union, which would be renamed to the World Union. This would also take the place of the United Nations. They were expecting the transition to take two to three months.

Michael reported that everyone in the world would be given a national ID and would have sixty days to obtain their ID card. In the United States, everyone, including children, would be required to go to their local DMV and register. At that time, they would receive a card with their national ID, their country ID, and their birthdate, as well as a biometric fingerprint of their right index finger. No one would be excluded from being registered.

Michael ended the broadcast by stating that he felt this was a positive move and would ultimately provide security and economic stability to the United States. He reported that Marcus Aldric would be having a live press conference tomorrow and would address the additional questions people would have concerning the World Union.

Olivia was flabbergasted: this was exactly what Pastor Thomas had spoken about in the meeting on Saturday. She had been so convinced that he was another doomsayer and that it would never come to be. Olivia called her mom on her cell phone as soon as the broadcast was over. The phone went right to voice mail, which was to be expected as her mother was probably with a patient. Olivia left a quick message stating, "Mom, call me when you get a chance." She turned the TV off and went to check on Matt. He was engrossed in his game and did not hear her come into the room.

"Hey, Matt, how is it going?"

He answered without turning from his computer screen, "Fine, what's up?"

"Nothing, just wanted to make sure you were doing okay."

Matt turned around and looked at Olivia with a perplexed look. "Why are you being so weird?"

"I'm not. I just feel responsible for you when Mom is at work, and sorry I asked."

Olivia then turned around and went back downstairs. She really wanted to talk to someone about what was happening and remembered she had exchanged phone numbers with the other members of the church. Olivia felt this was a pivotal moment in time and did not want to be alone. She had a sick feeling in the pit of her stomach. Everything that Pastor Thomas had warned them about had started. She wished she had taken notes to compare what was said and what was happening. Olivia, deep in thought, was startled when her cell phone rang. It was her mother.

"Hi, Mom."

"What's up, Olivia? You never call me at work."

"Did you see the news? There was a special report that interrupted my show earlier."

"Olivia, I'm at work; you know I am not watching TV. What was it about?"

Olivia then went on to describe to her mother what the newscaster had reported. Her mother remained silent throughout her recounting of the events. When Olivia was done, her mother stated, "Well, I guess Thomas was right. At least we will be prepared and will know what to expect in the near future."

"You have got to be kidding me, Mom! This is so scary, aren't you worried?"

"Olivia, worrying is not going to change the outcome. The main thing is to be prepared and know what we need to do in order to keep ourselves safe and to do as Pastor Thomas says to keep our faith. Listen, I have to get back to work. We can discuss this tomorrow. For tonight, I want you to try not to worry. I know that is not easy, but in the long run, everything will be all right."

"Okay, Mom, I'm glad you called. I feel better knowing that you are not freaking out. I love you."

"I love you too."

When Olivia got off the phone, she felt better. Her mother was right: there was no use in worrying about this tonight. She was anxious for the next meeting in town. In the meantime, she decided to call Clara. She found her number in her phone, and Clara picked up after the first ring.

"Hey, Olivia. I'm glad you called. I have been thinking about you the past couple of days."

"Really, you should have called me. I'm always home and could have used someone to talk to."

"I'm sorry. I will not hesitate to call you again. I just did not want to be pushy." Clara sounded truly apologetic.

"No, I'm sorry. I just have had a bad couple of days. It is not your fault. I was calling to see if you heard the news tonight."

"Who hasn't? They interrupted every media outlet to report it."

"I know it's crazy and scary. It seems that it is fitting in what Pastor Thomas has predicted would happen."

"Well, to be fair, it was John who actually predicted this through God in Revelation, but I know what you mean. It seems that Pastor Thomas was right in that it appears to be happening in the next few months," Clara said dryly.

"Isn't that scary to you?" Olivia asked.

"Not really. I am excited to go to heaven. I don't talk about this much, but I have lost several family members in the past couple of years. My grandparents both died from COVID-19 in 2020. That was very difficult. I was close to both of them. They were my mom's parents. When they died, my mom went through a depression. I never knew my father. He and my mother were never married. My grandparents helped raise me. My grandfather was like a father to me. So, after they died, not only had I to deal with their death, but my mother retreated into herself, and she really has not been the same since. So…I guess you would say I am ready to leave this world and join Jesus in heaven."

"I'm so sorry, Clara. It appears we have all been through a lot in the past few years. I'm excited to go to heaven also, but I am worried about the events that lead up to that moment."

"I think the best thing we can do is continue to meet with Pastor Thomas and learn as much as we can about what will be happening and figure it out from there. We cannot spend the next seven years worrying about what will happen. We just need to be prepared, as Pastor Thomas says."

"Thanks, Clara. I appreciate your positive attitude. It is easy for me to go down a negative path, and it helps when someone pulls me back and helps me stay focused on the grand prize."

"Anytime, Olivia. Well, I guess I will see you tomorrow night at church. You are still going, aren't you?"

"I wouldn't miss it. Good night, Clara."

Olivia hung up the phone, feeling better after her talk with both Clara and her mom. She ran upstairs and said goodnight to Matt, who was still busy playing with his friends online.

After brushing her teeth and washing her face, Olivia jumped into bed, hoping for a nightmare-free night of sleep.

## CHAPTER SEVEN

The next morning Olivia awoke, feeling refreshed. She had slept well and without any nightmares. Her mom was off for the day, so Olivia convinced her to go to North Georgia Premium Outlets, which was in Dawsonville, about an hour away. It had been over a year since she and her mother had actually gone shopping for clothes in person. She had ordered items online, but that was not the same. Matt did not want to go, so Elizabeth made arrangements with the neighbor Susan to check on him throughout the day. He did not feel he needed a babysitter, so she let him stay home alone.

Olivia was not only glad to get some new outfits but also excited with the chance to drive her new car. She really needed to get her license and was happy to get some practice driving.

They spent the whole day going from store to store, trying on outfits and shoes. While on a break, eating lunch, Elizabeth brought up the phone call last night, "You were really freaked out last night. Are you feeling better today?"

Olivia grimaced. "I know. I'm sorry for calling you at work. It just took me by surprise when the news came on and pretty much confirmed what Pastor Thomas was saying to us. I just needed to talk to you. Matt was no help. He seems completely oblivious to all of this, and I did not want to scare him."

"You know you can call me anytime. It is just hard to get away at work to talk."

Olivia grimaced again. "I know, I don't like to, though. I feel better today. I also talked to Clara last night, and she was a big help."

"I'm glad you are making friends here. I worry about you and Matt and just want both of you to be happy."

"We know, Mom. It is just going to take time. I am definitely missing my friends in Florida less and less if that makes you feel better." Olivia went on to tell her mother about her call with Kylie the other day and how she was left feeling more and more disconnected from her and that life.

"Well, it is not unusual for friends to drift apart when they live so far apart," Clara sympathized.

"I know, but for some reason, I did not think it would happen to us. I thought we would graduate from high school and go off to college together. It is just sad to imagine my life without her."

"I'm sorry, honey, you two have been friends for a long time. You don't have to give up on the friendship. Keep trying and see where it goes."

"I guess, but I don't want to have to be the one always trying. She never calls me anymore, and when I talk to her, she really does not seem interested in what I am doing or how things are going with me. It really feels one-sided," Olivia said solemnly.

Elizabeth got up, walked around the table, and gave Olivia a hug. "I wish you did not have to go through any of this, but believe it or not, things will get better. How about we finish shopping? It looks like we cleaned out the stores," she joked as she looked down at all the bags on the floor and the two chairs at their table.

"Sounds good. I really need to walk after all the food I just ate."

Saturday night finally arrived, and Olivia could not wait to hear what Pastor Thomas had to say. The Ahrens arrived about fifteen minutes early. Olivia immediately sought out Caleb and the other teens. She found them clustered in the back of the sanctuary. Everyone was there except Emma and Seth.

Olivia greeted the group, "Hey, guys, crazy week. I cannot believe what has been going on in the news."

Caleb nodded, saying, "I know. I did not think it would be this soon."

"I have been researching Marcus Aldric since the news broke, and it seems like he is our man," Clara added.

Daniel shook his head, stating, "I'm not sure. He seems like a great guy. If it was not for him and his company, some of us might not even be here to be having this conversation. We have all lost someone to the virus, and personally, I feel we owe Mr. Aldric our gratitude, not accusations of him being the Antichrist."

"That is exactly the person that would be the Antichrist. Someone who we are all indebted to, who comes across as a hero," Caleb responded.

"I agree. From what Pastor Thomas discussed last week, I feel that Marcus is the perfect candidate," Olivia interjected.

Marty also expressed her doubts, "I don't know what to think at this time, but I'm sure that Pastor Thomas will enlighten us and cannot wait to hear his thoughts on this."

"Well, let's get a seat, as the meeting is about to start," Clara directed.

Pastor Thomas started the meeting with breaking news, "Good evening, everyone. I know many of you want to discuss the events of the week and the news of Marcus Aldric. We will get to that, but I also wanted to share events that have been kept under wraps and have come to light a few hours ago. Apparently, the pope and the cardinal camerlengo both died during the Ebola outbreak. This news was not released to the general population. The Vatican was afraid it would cause worldwide disruption. The election of his successor has not occurred due to the virus running rampant in the Vatican."

Pastor Thomas went on to say that following the pope's death, 105 cardinals, which was 90 percent of the eligible cardinals to vote for the new pope, had died within days of the beginning of the conclave. Unbeknownst to the members of the papal conclave, one of the cardinals had been exposed to the virus but had never developed symptoms. He was deemed a carrier. At the present time, there was no current pope, and the Catholic Church was floundering for direction. Many of the archbishops had also died in the plague.

Pastor Thomas somberly reported, "The World Council of Religious Leaders were planning a meeting in October to discuss the turmoil happening throughout the world and the lack of leadership in many of the religious groups. Since the news that the pope had died, they decided to move the meeting to next week. The Institute for Religious Freedom and Tolerance is recommending electing one leader to help diminish the divide and promote understanding and unity among the different faiths. The meeting will be held at the United Nations building in New York City."

Olivia did not understand the seriousness of this news. She did not know much about the Catholic religion but, like everyone in the world, understood what an important role the pope had in the religious circles.

Pastor Thomas went on to describe the prophetic connection this had to the rise of the Antichrist.

"With the call for a one-world government and uniting all of the churches, it fits with John's description of the ruler having vast power and authority, which was given to him directly from

Satan himself. He will be followed by and receive worship from 'all the world' and will have 'authority over every tribe, people, language and nation.'²"

Pastor Thomas looked at the crowd and shook his head sadly. "With power over the government and religion, the Antichrist will have control over all nations and people."

Several hands went up in the crowd. Pastor Thomas began taking questions and answering to the best of his ability. One gentleman, whose name Olivia could not remember, asked, "What are we going to do about everyone being required to obtain a national ID card and taking a fingerprint of our right finger? This seems to go along with taking the mark of the beast."

Pastor Thomas responded, "Good question, Roger. I am not sure how this is going to correlate with the mark of the beast, but at present, you will not need to worry about it. According to Revelation 13:17, no one can buy or sell unless he has the mark, which is the name of the beast or the number of its name. However, many believe that this may be a more spiritual mark. Revelation, chapter eighteen, tells more of a 'mark of belonging.' The mark may be more of a figurative way of describing the loyalty of the Antichrist followers. It is difficult to actually say how this will look, as the Bible does not give enough details. We do know that without the mark, a person will not be able to buy food, find shelter, sell anything, or even get medical attention. This will not happen, though, until three and a half years after the start of the tribulation."

Another hand went up immediately.

"Yes, Tara?"

"So we should go and obtain the ID card that is required, as they said on the news?"

"Yes, as long as nothing else becomes of this, there should be no problem. The idea is that when it becomes required to take the mark of the beast, you will definitely know which side you are choosing. At this point, they are not asking you to pledge your allegiance to anyone. As I said, this may in the future be connected with the mark of the beast, but not today."

Pastor Thomas ended the meeting right at 8:00 p.m., "We will end for tonight. I hope to see you all in church tomorrow, and we will move to the second seal at next Saturday's meeting. It would be good if everyone read Revelation 6:3-4. Thank you all for coming."

The majority of people left the sanctuary talking among themselves. There were a few that stayed behind and were speaking with the pastor.

Olivia said goodbye to her friends and walked over to her mom. She was talking to the woman Pastor Thomas called Tara.

"Olivia, this is Tara. Tara, this is my daughter, Olivia. Could you please go find Matt? I think he went outside."

"Sure. Are you ready to leave now?"

"Yes, I will be right outside. If you want to wait in the car, I should be there in a couple of minutes."

Olivia found Matt sitting outside with the same boy he had been talking with last week after church.

"Hey, Matt, who's your friend?"

Matt gave her a derisive look and stated, "This is Mark. Mark, this is my sister Olivia. She happens to be a pain in the butt."

Olivia scowled, retorting, "Mom wants us to meet her in the car. Are you ready?"

"Sure. Hey, Mark, I will see you tomorrow. Give me a call later, though, and we can finish the game."

"Sounds good. See ya later," Mark replied, without even bothering to look up from the game he was focused on.

Olivia and Matt walked to the car silently. Their mother showed up a few minutes later, and they drove home in silence. Olivia and Elizabeth were caught up in their own thoughts, and Matt was engrossed in his game.

# Chapter Eight

And I saw a beast rising out of the sea, with ten horns and seven heads, with ten diadems on its horns and blasphemous names on its heads. And the beast that I saw was like a leopard; its feet were like a bear's, and its mouth was like a lion's mouth. And to it the dragon gave his power and his throne and great authority. One of its heads seemed to have a mortal wound, but its mortal wound was healed, and the whole earth marveled as they followed the beast. And they worshiped the dragon, for he had given his authority to the beast, and they worshiped the beast, saying, "Who is like the beast, and who can fight against it?" And the beast was given a mouth uttering haughty and blasphemous words, and it was allowed to exercise authority for forty-two months.

*Revelation 13:1-5 (ESV)*

## October 11, 2025

As the weeks went on, Olivia had developed a comfortable routine. She and Matt started back to school on August 25. They spent their mornings doing Zoom classroom meetings and the afternoons catching up on homework. Olivia usually would talk with her friends on the phone in the evenings, especially Clara and Caleb, and she actually looked forward to Saturday evening meetings in the church. The group, which usually consisted of herself, Emma,

Seth, Clara, Marty, Caleb, and occasionally Daniel, started getting together a half an hour before the actual meeting in order to catch up on what was going on in their lives. Olivia's mother did not mind going early, but Matt would often grumble until he convinced his friend Mark to go early also. Every Monday, Olivia and her friends would meet at another restaurant downtown and then go for a walk around Blue Ridge City Park. The air was cooler, and Olivia actually enjoyed the fall weather, though she was used to Sarasota being warm for the majority of the year.

Caleb would often drive her, as she still had not gotten her license. Olivia had been practicing driving and felt that she would be ready to take the test in the next couple of weeks. During this time, Olivia and Caleb had grown closer. He was funny, smart, caring, and it did not hurt that he was cute too. Olivia enjoyed spending time with him. They spent much of their time discussing the events going on in the world but also talked about their childhood and what their plans were for the future. He seemed to genuinely care about what she thought, which was quite different from her old friends in Florida. The longer she was away from them and interacting with her new friends, the more she realized how superficial her old friendships were. She had not talked to Kylie in days. Olivia had reached out to her a few times in the past few weeks, but Kylie always seemed busy or distracted. There were many times her calls went right to voice mail, and she got no call back. Olivia recognized that Kylie was going through a difficult time, as her caregivers had decided to move back to New York. Kylie was hoping that she could convince them to change their minds, but at this point, it looked like it was a done deal and she would be moving before Christmas.

Marcus Aldric was in the news every day. He had given several press conferences, reassuring Americans that everything would get back to normal, and he was hoping that the expansion of the European Union would help in the process. He was appointed by national leaders to be the president of the World Union.

The World Council of Religious Leaders had met in New York City. They were holding an election in the next couple of days to select a leader to oversee a committee of twelve that would consist of a representative from the major religious groups: Christianity, Islam, Hinduism, Buddhism, Sikhism, Taoism, Judaism, Confucianism, Bahá'í, Shinto, Jainism, and Zoroastrianism. The council reported that their aim was to promote religious freedom and tolerance.

Pastor Thomas had focused the past couple of meetings on the Antichrist but also began discussing the false prophet, warning the group that Jesus had foretold the disciples in Matthew that many will come in His name, claiming to be Christ, and will lead many astray.

He reminded the group that the first seven seals would all take place within the first three and a half years of the tribulation. Olivia had begun reading Revelation and had focused her attention on the seven seals. She knew that none of this would start until a peace agreement was initiated between Israel and some other country, which she could not remember, but she was still petrified of what was to come, especially when she read more about the seven seals and the fact that the second seal was specifically about war.

All of the members of the church had gone to the DMV to be registered and were given a national ID. Many of them were still very suspicious that this was related to the mark of the Antichrist, but Pastor Thomas continued to reassure them. Elizabeth had taken Olivia and Matthew to the DMV shortly after the decree was enacted back in August. Olivia did not know how to feel about this. She agreed with many of the others that somehow this would eventually be connected to the mark of the beast. She had to keep reminding herself of Pastor Thomas's declaration that taking the mark of the beast would be a deliberate choice they would make and that it would not happen until they were halfway through the tribulation. Pastor Thomas also insisted that by that time, the believers would be raptured up to heaven. He had been right on so many things so far, and she was going to continue to trust him.

Tonight, Pastor Thomas indicated that he would be sharing updated news. Olivia was anxious to hear what he had to say. The Ahrens arrived at 6:30 p.m. at the church, and Olivia immediately sought out her friends. Matt went off with Mark and another boy that Olivia did not recognize. Elizabeth went to talk to some of the other women, who were setting up coffee and cookies on a table in the back.

All the teenagers, including Daniel, were present tonight. Olivia assumed that they had all heard that Pastor Thomas had news to share and were anxious to hear it firsthand.

The meeting started right at 7:00 p.m. The sanctuary was very quiet, and everyone sitting in the pews was quite somber.

Pastor Thomas started the meeting by welcoming everyone. There were a few new members, and he had them introduce themselves prior to starting. First up was a young couple, Millie and Austin. They both grew up in Blue Ridge and heard about the meeting from their neighbors. Millie had grown up Catholic but stated she had a strong urge to hear what Pastor Thomas was preaching. Austin stated he was not a regular churchgoer. Millie had begged him to come with her tonight, but he appeared suspicious, informing the audience, "I'm open to hear what you say, but I'm not sure about any of it."

Pastor Thomas nodded and said understandingly, "This is a very difficult topic, and I do not expect you to believe everything I say, but know that everything I am preaching is straight out of the Bible."

"Well, you see, that is the problem. I am not sure I even believe the Bible. I came for Millie, and I will listen to what you have to say and make my opinion."

"That's all I can ask of you. We are glad that you came tonight."

The other new member was a single woman named Lydia. She was a widow and had recently moved to Blue Ridge to be closer to her son Clive and his wife Tricia, who were members of the church.

Once the church went around and introduced themselves, Pastor Thomas began speaking, "I'm sure you all want me to get right to the updated news I have. So, I won't waste time with pleasantries. It appears that the World Council of Religious Leaders had an election late last evening and elected a leader, as well as the twelve representatives from each of the major religious groups. The new leader is from Italy. They apparently elected a Christian leader, as Christianity is the world's most popular religious group and has over two billion followers. The newly appointed leader is from the Catholic religion and is a cardinal. He was one of the few that survived Ebola when it hit the cardinals during the concave. His name is Allesandro D'Angelo, and he had been appointed the archpriest of Saint Peter's Basilica just prior to the outbreak."

Pastor Thomas dragged his hand through his hair and paused. His expression was grim. "The previous archpriest had died from a heart attack at a relatively young age of fifty-eight. A leader was also elected for each of the other religious groups."

When Pastor Thomas finished, many people raised their hands up in the air to ask questions. Everyone wanted to know if Allesandro D'Angelo was who John was referencing in Revelation as the "false prophet."

Pastor Thomas responded solemnly, "Yes, I do believe that. I think he will use religion to bring the world over to unison with the Antichrist. He will encourage others to follow the Antichrist, who will focus on politics, and the false prophet's emphasis will be on religion. John actually talks about three beasts who will make up 'The Unholy Trinity.' One is a dragon, Satan, the second is the Antichrist, and the third member of this group 'claims to speak for God'[3] but is a false prophet. After the initial three and a half years, the false prophet will suffer a deadly injury and will return to life, which will mimic Christ's resurrection, and this will lend credibility to his lies."

The questions continued for another forty-five minutes until Pastor Thomas ended the meeting. Millie and Austin left immediately after the meeting. The rest of the members stood around for a while, talking among themselves.

Olivia and the other teenagers walked outside to enjoy the brisk clean air.

Caleb was the first to break the silence, "What do you, guys, think?"

Daniel looked dubious and shared, "We really do not have any proof that any of this is going to amount to anything. I feel like I have been hearing about the end of the world for years since I was born. Every religious show my mom watches has someone on there with a prophecy about the end times."

Emma nodded in agreement. "I really am kind of tired of hearing all of this. We should not have to be dealing with any of it. I am a senior and would just like to enjoy my last year of high school and get ready to go away to college. With so many kids doing remote learning, it is not how I imagined senior year would be. They probably will not even let us have a prom again this year."

Marty argued, "What we want to happen and what is going to happen are two different things. You can wish that the evidence Pastor Thomas has been presenting to us is not going to happen, but that does not mean it will not. I, for one, would rather have all the information and be prepared. It seems to me that everything he has told us so far directly correlates with the prophecy of the Bible."

Clara, Seth, Olivia, and Caleb all agreed with Marty. They continued on with the debate until Marty's father and Elizabeth's mother found them outside.

"Time to go, Olivia. Matt's waiting in the car."

"Okay, bye, guys, see you next tomorrow at church," Olivia responded.

Olivia drove to church, so she got into the driver's seat. She still could not believe the Volkswagen was hers. It was a quiet drive home, so Olivia had a chance to mull over what Pastor Thomas had said tonight. She planned to research the new head of the World Council of Religious Leaders, but that could wait till tomorrow. Tonight she would go home and watch some mindless show on TV and not worry about anything.

## Chapter Nine

### December 12, 2025

"Mom, can you believe this!" Olivia exclaimed while looking at her laptop.

"What are you talking about?" Elizabeth was trying to eat a quick meal before running out the door to go to work.

"There is a big headline on the news feed saying that the World Council of Religious Leaders has brokered a peace agreement with Israel, which includes negotiating territory in exchange for peace with the Palestinians. According to the article, they have come up with a solution of two separate states that would give Palestine most of the West Bank. They also are allowing a Palestinian capital in East Jerusalem. The Jews will be allowed to build a temple on the Temple Mount, and there will be no restrictions for any religion to worship there."

Elizabeth stopped eating and leaned forward, intrigued. "Wow, that is definitely interesting news. Does it say anything else?"

"They are planning to build the temple about 200 meters south of the Dome of the Rock, which has access to the Gihon freshwater spring. The new leader of the World Council of Religious Leaders, as well as Marcus Aldric, have visions of transforming the Temple Mount to its original sacred role as a place of worship that will be shared by Jews, Muslims, and Christians."

Olivia continued on, "Of course, there are many who are objecting to rebuilding the temple, especially in regard to the location. Allesandro D'Angelo's argument is that Jewish doctrine emphasizes the role of a prophet in regard to rebuilding the temple. This prophet would have complete authority, which includes the discretion to specify the temple's precise location, regardless of any Jewish traditions. D'Angelo relates that he had a holy revelation that the temple is to be rebuilt on the Temple Mount in peaceful proximity to the dome, the Aqsa Mosque, and nearby Christian shrines. The peace agreement will be signed today, as Hanukkah will begin tomorrow at sunset." Olivia finished reading the report with a heavy sigh. "This is crazy, Mom. This is exactly what Pastor Thomas had told us would happen."

"I can't say I'm surprised, Olivia. He has been spot on with many of his predictions thus far. I am just so glad that he reached out to me to come to the meetings at the church. Otherwise, we would be blissfully unaware, which would not have been good for our eternal future."

Elizabeth got up from the table and put her plate in the dishwasher. "I have to get to work. I'm going upstairs to tell Matt goodbye. I'll be right back."

Olivia had spent the last couple of months in a comfortable routine. She had finally taken and passed her driving test and felt a new sense of freedom. She was actually looking forward to the holiday events coming up. Olivia and the other teens had planned a small Christmas party at the church for next Friday evening. Clara had gone shopping with her, and they each bought a new outfit for the party. Until this afternoon, she had been able to put thoughts of the tribulation out of her head, except for when she attended the meetings at church. Even those had been decreased to every month as everyone had been busy with the holidays.

Olivia, Elizabeth, and Matt had celebrated Thanksgiving with Caleb and his dad. It was definitely much more joyful than the previous Thanksgiving, which had been their first without Katie and her father. Olivia still thought of them often, but the grief had lessened, and she was more apt to think of the good times they had together.

Elizabeth and Matthew also seemed to be doing much better. Matt had his new friends and spent less time alone in his room. He still played a lot of video games, but it was no longer a strictly solitary activity. Elizabeth had made friends at work and at church and was frequently going out for lunch or coffee on her days off.

This news just brought her back to the reality of what was to come in the near future. According to Pastor Thomas, once the treaty was signed, the seven-year tribulation would begin. That meant that the second seal would be opened, and that involved war.

"All right, I'm leaving now. There is a frozen pizza in the freezer or taquitos that you two can have later." Elizabeth gave Olivia a quick hug, grabbed her coat, and yelled out, "Love you!" as she walked out the door to the garage.

As soon as Elizabeth left, Olivia called Caleb to discuss what she had just read.

Caleb answered right away, "Hey, Olivia, what's up?"

"Did you hear the news today about the peace agreement?"

Caleb was silent for a second, and when he answered, his voice was grim, "Yeah, Dad and I have been talking about it since the news broke today."

"What is he saying?"

"Well, you know him. He basically is telling me that this was expected, but he is still surprised at how fast everything is moving. I am almost relieved that it has started, as at times I feel that I am just waiting for the next shoe to drop, and now that it has, we can deal with it."

Olivia thought for a second and agreed with Caleb, "You are right. We knew it was coming, although, at times, I was able to actually forget about it, and now we know we have three and a half years to get through. I just hope your dad is right about the rapture taking place before the really bad stuff starts happening. I do not want to be around after that."

Caleb snickered, "I agree. As bad as these first three and a half years are, they are nothing compared to the end of the tribulation. Are you coming to the meeting tomorrow?"

"Yes, I will definitely be there."

Olivia and Caleb hung up, and she went back to doing her homework, which was interrupted earlier by the news alerts on her laptop.

Saturday evening came, and Olivia and her family arrived at the church a few minutes before 6:30 p.m. There were several people there that Olivia did not recognize, although she noted that Millie had returned, but Austin was not with her tonight. She questioned her mom about all the new people.

"Well, according to my sources, several of the church members have been recruiting new people and witnessing to them. I think, with all of the events happening in the world, people want answers. For those that had been on the fence, they see the prophecies of the Bible play out and want to make the right choices," Elizabeth responded.

Olivia frowned. "I feel bad, Pastor Thomas had asked us to go out and minister to those we love and care about at that first meeting, and I have done nothing."

Elizabeth shook her head. "You cannot say you have done nothing. Since we started coming to these meetings, you have been open, participatory, and supportive of your friends. Have you gone out on the streets and preached? No, but the things you are doing will have a lasting impact. I am just so happy that you are coming to the meetings with me and have taken an active interest in what is going on."

Olivia smiled at her mom. "Thanks. I just wish I could do more."

"You will—when the time comes. For now, just keep doing what you have been doing." Elizabeth smiled encouragingly.

Pastor Thomas greeted everyone and, unlike in the past, did not ask the new members to introduce themselves. He immediately brought up the breaking news regarding the peace agreement: "I know you all probably heard the news yesterday. I think, for tonight, I will just take questions, and we can go from there. Let me start by saying that this was expected. Now that the peace agreement has been signed, as well as the Antichrist and the false prophet have been identified, I can safely say the clock has started for the tribulation. Now, who has questions?"

Immediately hands went up around the room. Pastor Thomas spent the next hour answering questions and attempting to reassure everyone that they would be protected. Many questions were centered on what they could expect in the next few months.

Pastor Thomas shook his head. "We can expect the second seal to be open and war to occur, but how that will look, I do not know. I also do not know what the time frame will be. I anticipate that there will be a period of peace for the next few months to ensure that the Antichrist and false prophet can lull us all into a false sense of security. I am not sure how long that will last, but we will be prepared. Next meeting, I will focus on the second seal. We will not meet again until January. I want you all to have a good holiday season. Keep reading the Bible and let your family, friends, and even strangers know what will be coming to pass so they can be prepared. Thanks, everyone, for coming. I hope to see everyone in church tomorrow." With that, Pastor Thomas walked off the stage and exited the church, though he usually stayed afterward to talk to the members.

Olivia found Caleb and questioned him, "Is everything okay with your father? He seemed a little more subdued tonight, and he left right after the meeting."

Caleb sucked in a deep breath. "Well, today is the anniversary of the day my mom developed symptoms from Ebola. She actually died on Christmas Eve. I think my dad is just having a difficult time dealing with that and everything else that is going on in the world. He doesn't talk about it, but I can just tell."

Olivia placed her hand on Caleb's shoulder. "I am so sorry. This must be a very difficult time for both of you. Is there anything I can do?"

Caleb gave her a tight smile. "No, I appreciate that. I think just staying busy and trying to keep my mind off of it is the best medicine. I really appreciate your friendship, and it does help to talk to you, as you know exactly how I am feeling."

Olivia grimaced. "I wish I didn't, but we cannot change the past. It has really helped having you all in my life. Four months ago, I did not think that I would ever be happy again, and look at me now. I actually think that, in some ways, I am happier. All that superficial stuff I worried about no longer seems important. Don't get me wrong: I still like to go shopping," she said with a grin.

Caleb smiled back. "I haven't met a woman who doesn't. I better go, though. I'm going to spend time with my dad, see if he wants to talk about my mom."

"Okay, I will see you tomorrow. Have a good night, Caleb."

With one last wave, Caleb walked toward the exit. Olivia watched him go till he was out the door. She found the rest of the group huddled in the back of the church by the cookies and coffee.

Olivia stood for a while talking with Emma, Seth, Clara, Marty, and Daniel until her mother came to get her.

While walking out of the church, Olivia questioned her mother about Austin and if she knew why he did not return. Elizabeth was evasive, "All Millie said was that he did not believe in the Bible and felt all the talk about the tribulation was just a scare tactic for religious leaders to get people to come to church and donate money."

"Wow. That is quite a stretch. It is amazing to think that there will be people out there who will follow both the Antichrist and the false prophet. I always thought everyone should see right through them, but when you hear that even people who grew up in church are still susceptible to their lies, that really makes you wonder about those that have not grown up learning about Jesus."

"Yes, it is amazing what people choose to believe. I hope that we can convince enough of our friends and family in the next three and a half years. I have been talking to Grandma and Grandpa about the tribulation, and they are definitely believers, but I am not so sure about aunt Shari. She was always the doubter."

"I guess I should be reaching out to my friends in Sarasota, but I have not really talked to any of them, except for Kylie, since we moved. It was just too hard. What do you think, should I call Peyton, Max, and Audrey?"

"I think that we should try to reach as many people as possible. Now is not the time to worry about what they think about you. We need to ensure that we have done everything in our power to educate them on what is coming, and they need to accept Jesus as their Lord and Savior."

Matt spoke up from the back seat, "I will leave that to you two. I have hard enough time keeping up with my schoolwork and trying to beat Mark at the new Mario Kart."

"Very funny. You will need to do your part, too, young man," Elizabeth replied sternly.

Matt just responded with, "Whatever."

When Olivia got home, she decided to call Kylie and let her know what was going on. The call went right to voice mail. She planned to try again tomorrow and would not give up until she actually talked with her.

Olivia went to bed that night somewhat troubled, worried about the future but also concerned that she had not done her part to spread the gospel.

## Chapter Ten

### December 19, 2025

Clara came over Friday night so she and Olivia could get ready for the party together. They were both excited to actually do something fun and not have to worry about all the doom and gloom that had been surrounding everyone for the past year and a half. All their friends were going. Emma was just happy to be able to dress up, as homecoming and the prom were canceled for this year.

Olivia agreed to have Clara do her makeup and brought her makeup bag with her. Olivia usually just wore a little cover-up and mascara. When Clara was done, Olivia could hardly believe she was looking at herself in the mirror. Her light-blue eyes popped, and the contouring made her high cheekbones even more prominent. Olivia wished that Katie were here to see how much she had grown over the past year. She quickly put those thoughts away and focused on getting dressed for the party.

When Olivia and Clara were done getting dressed, they both looked in the full-length mirror that hung from Olivia's closet.

"Wow, we look good, don't we?" Clara said with a cheeky smile.

"I've got to say we do clean up well. Thanks so much for doing my makeup."

Olivia and Clara spent the next few minutes looking in the mirror and adjusting their outfits. Clara was wearing a red fit-and-flare dress that came to just above her knees. It had a sweetheart neckline and looked fantastic next to her dark skin. Clara normally wore her long hair curly and loose, but tonight had it pulled back into a high ponytail that fell to her midback.

Olivia had chosen a champagne-colored short A-line skirt that flared out above her knees. It had a sweetheart neckline with three straps that graced her shoulders and attached to the open back and banded waistline. With her makeup done perfectly and her long hair styled in a braided and twisted messy bun, she felt like a princess.

Elizabeth smiled broadly at the girls as they walked downstairs. "Oh my gosh, you girls look so lovely. Let me take some pictures before you leave."

The girls posed in front of the Christmas tree and outside on the deck. There had been a light snowfall earlier in the day, and the moon sparkled off the snowflakes. Elizabeth took multiple pictures until Olivia halted the photo shoot, "Enough, Mom, we are going to be late, and I am freezing."

"All right, it is just so nice to actually have you do something for a change that seems so normal. I hope you girls plan on wearing your coats tonight."

"Definitely. Thanks, Mom. We will be home around eleven."

"Thanks, Mrs. Ahren, for letting me spend the night. We will see you later," Clara called out as they walked to the car.

Clara drove to the party, as Olivia did not feel comfortable driving on snow yet. She never had to deal with it in Sarasota. Olivia was looking forward to a white Christmas, but beyond that, she was not a fan of snow.

They arrived at the church a few minutes after 7:00 p.m. They placed their coats on the table upstairs and then walked down to the basement where the party was being held. Olivia was surprised at how crowded the recreation room was already, but she was able to spot Caleb, Marty, Emma, and Seth standing next to the food table. She did not see Daniel, but she knew he was planning on attending.

Clara and Olivia walked over to their friends. Caleb gave a low whistle when he looked up from his plate and noticed the girls. "You guys look amazing."

Clara and Olivia both thanked Caleb. Olivia smiled. "You all look great. Emma and Marty, I love your dresses."

Emma looked lovely in a black sequined close-fitting dress that made her blonde hair and pale-gray eyes stand out more so than usual. Marty was wearing a sparkly navy-blue off-the-shoulder dress with a full skirt that fell right to her knees. Her auburn hair was up in a messy side bun.

Caleb looked very handsome in a charcoal-gray suit with a white button-down shirt and a red tie. His black hair was styled to be messy with a little bit of curl in the longer top hair. The sides were cut neat and short. Seth was wearing black dress pants, a white button-down shirt, and a black-and-red tie. His blond hair was held in place with gel.

Clara complimented the guys, "You two look great tonight. Where's Daniel?"

Caleb shrugged his shoulders. "I haven't seen him yet. He mentioned he might be late, although he did not say why."

Olivia checked out the food table. The church had taken donations and had the food catered from a local restaurant. There was a wide variety of sandwiches, chicken wings, chicken tenders, dips, and desserts. There was also a drink table with sodas and juices. She opted to get a drink and save eating till later. She did not want to ruin her makeup this early in the night.

One of the church members, Jeff Kovac, was a DJ and donated his services for free for the party. He had begun playing some top forty songs, and a few of the kids were already out on the dance floor.

Clara grabbed Olivia's hand and gestured to the others. "Come on, let's hit the dance floor before it gets too crowded."

Seth declined, offering to hold their spot near the food, but Caleb joined the girls.

When a slow song came on, Caleb looked over to Olivia. "Shall we?" Suddenly nervous, she just nodded. Caleb reached for her hand and pulled her into his arms. Olivia smiled and wrapped her arms around his neck. They fell in step, letting the rhythm control their movements. Olivia felt like everyone else disappeared around them and like it was just the two of them in the rec room of the church. Once the song ended, they headed to the food table. They each got a plate and ate in silence. Clara and Emma soon joined them.

Daniel showed up a few hours into the party, with no explanation as to why he had been so late. Olivia noted that he appeared a little glassy-eyed and was acting strange. He did not stay long and left without saying goodbye to anyone. No one commented on his strange behavior, and Olivia soon put it out of her head.

A few hours later, the partygoers had dispersed, and there were only a few stragglers left. It was close to 11:00 p.m., so Clara and Olivia said their goodbyes. Caleb walked them out to Clara's car. He gave Clara a hug goodbye as she got in the car. He opened Olivia's car door and grabbed her hand.

"I had a really good time tonight, Olivia. Maybe we can go out, just the two of us, during Christmas break."

"I would love that. I had fun. It almost felt like we were just normal kids again."

Caleb leaned in and gave her a kiss on the cheek. "I will give you a call tomorrow, and we can make plans."

Olivia got into the car, grinning, and Clara just gave her a knowing look and shook her head.

# CHAPTER ELEVEN

"And I will appoint my two witnesses, and they will prophesy for 1,260 days, clothed in sackcloth." They are "the two olive trees" and the two lampstands, and "they stand before the Lord of the earth." If anyone tries to harm them, fire comes from their mouths and devours their enemies. This is how anyone who wants to harm them must die. They have power to shut up the heavens so that it will not rain during the time they are prophesying; and they have power to turn the waters into blood and to strike the earth with every kind of plague as often as they want.

*Revelation 11:3-6*

## January 2, 2026

Olivia woke that morning, feeling refreshed and ready to take on the day. She lay in bed for a while, reflecting on the past couple of weeks. It was the last official day of winter vacation. She had enjoyed the break from school and had spent a lot of time just hanging out with her friends. She and Caleb had gone out a few times to eat and walk around the park. They were taking things slowly. He would drop her off at home with a hug and a kiss on the cheek.

Emma had a new boyfriend, so she had been spending the majority of her free time with him. Since the Christmas party at church, Daniel had avoided the group. He also had not been attending church. Caleb thought that Daniel had been hanging out with some seniors from school who were not the best influence. Pastor Thomas had not scheduled another Saturday night meeting until the holidays were over. The next meeting was scheduled for tomorrow. Olivia was curious whether Daniel would show up or not.

Christmas was low-keyed with just the three of them. Elizabeth had gone all out and made a ham and a turkey with all the sides. It was a relaxing and carefree day, although quite different from their Christmases in the past. Prior to the outbreak, Elizabeth would spend thousands on Christmas gifts for the kids. There were definitely fewer presents this year, but Olivia did not feel she was missing out, and on the contrary, she felt more satisfied this year. It always seemed in the past that it was a competition with her other friends of who got more, but this year it did not seem to matter. With everything going on, Olivia was just happy that she was able to spend the day with her family. She felt her priorities had changed and felt she was a better person because of it. That evening Olivia had gone to Caleb's, and they exchanged gifts. Caleb had surprised Olivia with a beautiful yellow-and-white gold cross pendant and a matching pair of earrings. She had given him the newest version of AirPods, as he had accidentally washed his. She had also given him a hoodie from Hollister.

She invited their small group of friends, which consisted of Clara, Caleb, Seth, Emma, and Marty, over for New Year's Eve. Daniel had declined, stating he had other plans. Emma brought her new boyfriend, Liam. Olivia had a great time, and it was nice to bring in the New Year with her new best friends.

Olivia was brought back to the present day with her mom yelling for her and Matt to come down for breakfast. It was almost

9:00 a.m., and the room had a slight chill to it. Olivia begrudgingly got out of bed.

After finishing in the bathroom, she tromped downstairs.

"Why do I have to get up so early? It is my last day of vacation!"

"I thought you would want something nice for your last day. I made you your favorite, French toast roll-ups with strawberries."

"I do like those. Okay, you win. I was awake anyway. I was just enjoying lying in bed, thinking about the past couple of weeks."

"What are your plans for today?" Elizabeth asked while fixing a plate of food for Olivia.

"Not much. I was just hoping to hang out. I think Clara may come by later. It's too cold outside to do anything," Olivia grumbled.

Elizabeth rolled her eyes. "You are such a Florida girl. Your friends here would laugh at you. There is not even snow on the ground, and I think it is supposed to be forty-five today."

Matt wandered into the kitchen and eyed the French toast. "Oh, yay, my favorite." Then proceeded to heap his plate full.

"I don't know how you stay so skinny with all the food you eat," Olivia observed.

Matt grinned, "I'm still growing."

Elizabeth groaned, "I hope not. I cannot afford to keep buying you new clothes."

After breakfast, Olivia went on her laptop to check her social media when she came across breaking news. According to the news report, construction on the Jewish temple started today. They anticipated it would take over two years to build and were hoping to have it completed by March 2029, just in time for Passover. The Sanhedrin were taking steps necessary for reinstating future temple service, including restoring the sacred red heifer to Israel. According to the Bible, the red heifer's ashes mixed with water is a necessary element for purifying Jews to enable them to do service in the temple. The Temple Institute's School was training certified, DNA-tested Kohen (descendants of the high priest Aaron) to perform the temple duties.

Although the majority of the Jewish community was celebrating the temple being rebuilt, there were others that were not very pleased with this news. There had been rioters and protestors outside the Mughrabi Gate near the Western Wall. The news of the temple being built had created new tension between the Muslims and the Jews. In preparation for the potential escalation of tension, the Israeli police, who managed the Temple Mount, had increased the number of guards at all the entrances and exits.

Olivia continued to scroll through different articles, many reporting the same news. Everyone was worried that war would break out, but others were celebrating the new temple. She did find one article that mentioned two older gentlemen standing outside the mob of protestors. They were dressed in large flowing black tunics, resembling sackcloth, belted at the waist with a band of leather. The two men were preaching the coming of Jesus Christ and the need for the sinners to repent and accept Jesus Christ as their Lord and Savior. Some of the protestors ignored them, but others yelled and threw rocks at them. The two men stood steadfast through it all and continued to preach, unfazed by the protestors' actions.

Olivia knew right away that the men the article was referring to were the two witnesses that Pastor Thomas had spoken about. She could not remember exactly what he had said about them but knew that they were to preach in Jerusalem for three and a half years and that then they would be killed and resurrected.

The doorbell rang as Olivia was googling the two witnesses on her laptop. Her mom answered the door and directed Clara into the living room.

Olivia greeted Clara and motioned for her to sit down next to her on the sofa. "Did you see the news this morning?" she questioned her.

"No, I was listening to music on my phone on the way over. I didn't even have the radio on. Why, what's up?" Clara leaned forward, intrigued.

Olivia turned her laptop to face Clara and had her read some of the articles regarding the temple and the two witnesses that had popped up on her news feed.

After Clara finished reading, she turned to Olivia. "That's crazy. It is amazing how accurate Pastor Thomas has been. I'm glad we are meeting tomorrow at the church. I would really like to hear from him what he thinks about all of this."

Olivia nodded. "Yeah, me too. I am interested in the second seal, which is what he is planning on talking about tomorrow. From what I understand, it means war is coming. My feeling is that the next couple of years are definitely not going to be easy, and I am getting kind of scared of what is going to happen."

Clara looked grim. "I totally agree. How about we put away the laptop today and go for a ride? There are some waterfalls that I would like to show you. We can do some hiking. The weather is perfect today—not too hot and not too cold."

"Can I go with you?" Matt yelled from the kitchen.

Clara looked at Olivia, who smiled and nodded.

"Sure, Matt, as long as you behave," Clara agreed with a grin.

The three spent the day driving around Blue Ridge with Clara showing them different waterfalls throughout the area. They stopped and had lunch at a café downtown and headed home around 4:30 p.m. Clara stayed for dinner, and by the time Olivia went to bed, she was exhausted from the day. She had enjoyed getting out of the house and spending time with Clara. Matt actually was fun and did not get on her nerves once while they were out. She thought to herself, *Maybe he is finally maturing*. With that thought, she turned off her light and went to sleep.

## Chapter Twelve

When the Lamb opened the second seal, I heard the second living creature say, "Come!" Then another horse came out, a fiery red one. Its rider was given power to take peace from the earth and to make people kill each other. To him was given a large sword.

*Revelation 6:3-4*

The next evening Olivia, Elizabeth, and Matthew attended the meeting at the church. Prior to the meeting, several small groups had formed to discuss the news from yesterday. Elizabeth joined a group of women, and Matt went off with Mark to play video games. Olivia found her friends and joined the group.

After greeting everyone, Olivia asked, "I know everyone is talking about the temple, but did anyone see the news about the two prophets outside the Temple Mount?"

Emma responded with a nod of her head, adding, "Yes, and I was hoping that Pastor Thomas talks about that this evening."

Caleb dragged his hand through his hair. "I'm sure he will. He had asked me if I had seen the news. My dad is keeping track of everything going on and definitely wants us all to be kept informed."

Clara smiled sadly. "He has been great. I just wish he did not have to. I was anxious for the tribulation to begin, as I am looking forward to going to heaven, but now that it is here, I am scared. The thought of war has me losing sleep. I don't want to lose any of you or my family."

The group all agreed that these were definitely scary times. They talked for a while and then went to sit down near the front, as Pastor Thomas was starting the meeting.

The church immediately got quiet when Pastor Thomas stood at the pulpit. He had brought out the whiteboard from the previous meeting and began discussing the seven seals and the first half of the tribulation.

Pastor Thomas put a check mark next to the line, "First seal: white horse, Antichrist." "Well, the first seal has definitely been broken, and the tribulation has begun. We need to be prepared for the breaking of the second seal. This can occur tomorrow, next month, or next year. There is no set date other than it will happen within the next three and a half years. So what we have so far is that the Antichrist and the false prophet have shown themselves, the peace treaty with Israel and Palestine has been signed, and the temple is being rebuilt. The other sign is that the two witnesses have arrived and are currently prophesizing outside the Temple Mount."

A hand went up in the audience. Pastor Thomas stopped and allowed them to ask their question. A gentleman in the front row asked, "Can you go into more detail about the two witnesses and who they are?"

Pastor Thomas nodded. "So, according to the book of Revelation, there will be two witnesses who will prophesy for forty-two months. They will bring plagues upon the earth and will be unable to be killed. On the last day of the forty-two months, according to Daniel's prophecy, the Antichrist will go into the temple in Jerusalem and stop the sacrifices that will have resumed. The Antichrist will then declare himself to be God and will kill the two witnesses. Given that no one had been able to kill them for the past three and a half years, the world will see the Antichrist as the most powerful man on earth. The Bible states that people from all nations will see their dead bodies and will rejoice and make merry. After the two prophets lie dead in the streets of Jerusalem for three and a half days, they will be resurrected and will ascend into heaven as their enemies watch."

Another hand went up in the audience. This time it was Millie. She asked, "I have read that the two prophets are Enoch and Elijah because they never actually died and were brought directly to heaven."

"That is a good question, Millie. The Bible never indicates who the two witnesses are. Of course, many have speculated, and the most common belief is that they are Enoch and Elijah, but again there is no clear evidence in the Bible naming them. Others think it will be Moses and Elijah."

Pastor Thomas continued to answer questions about the two witnesses for another half an hour when he cut the questions short, "I really want to discuss the second seal for the next thirty minutes, so we will table the questions about the two witnesses for tonight."

Pastor Thomas explained that despite the promises of peace from the Antichrist, a red rider on a horse would slay a great number of people. He related this to Christ's explanation in the book of Matthew that people would "hear of wars and rumors of wars"[4] and that "nation will rise against nation."[5]

"At this point, I really feel we need to be prepared for war, and with that, famine will come next. I am asking all of you to start storing canned goods and enough food for a couple of years. There is no way we can know how long the famine will last, and we really need to be prepared. If anyone is having any financial stressors, we will work with the church to help organize food drives as well as donations to those in need."

Lydia spoke up from the back, "I have a garden and love to can. I have way more than myself and my family will ever need. I am glad to donate whatever I have left over."

Several others spoke up and agreed to donate whatever they had left over. Many had gardens and often gave away their food anyway.

Olivia was pleasantly surprised at how quickly everyone spoke up and volunteered to help each other out. It was nice to see a community work together.

The meeting continued on till 8:00 p.m., and when it was over, everyone quickly dispersed and left for home.

The Ahrens did not stick around but left right after the meeting. Olivia had driven separately as she had made plans to stay at Clara's house for the night. Clara had given her directions, and Olivia planned to drive straight there after the meeting.

Caleb held Olivia's hand as he walked her out to her car. They did not speak until they reached her Volkswagen.

Olivia broke the silence, "It was really nice how the church seems to be working together to make sure that everyone will have enough food in preparation for the upcoming famine. I am not sure people in Sarasota would have done that, or at least not my group of friends."

"That is what I love about this town and our church. Everyone cares about each other and wants to make sure we get through this. I'm just worried about the people in our community that have no idea what is coming. I really feel that we need to be reaching out to others in our town."

"We had discussed this when I first started to come to these meetings, but I have definitely not acted on it. There are friends of mine from Florida that I have totally ghosted, as well as cousins and family up north. I feel like I have been so self-focused that I have neglected my responsibility in letting others know what is coming," Olivia responded somberly.

"Well, it is definitely not too late. Maybe we can work together with the rest of the gang to get the word out." Caleb responded encouragingly.

Olivia offered a bright smile, acknowledging, "I think that is a great idea. Maybe, after church tomorrow, we can get together and come up with a plan?"

"Perfect. I will talk to my dad tonight to see if he has any ideas on how we can go about doing this."

"Great, I'll see you tomorrow. I'm sure Clara is wondering where I am. She probably thinks I got lost, which may still happen," Olivia said with a grin.

"Okay, I'll see you tomorrow."

Caleb leaned in and gave her a quick kiss on the lips. It was just a fleeting moment, but Olivia's heart began to race. She fumbled for her keys and unlocked her door. Caleb stepped back, looking unsure of himself.

"I'm sorry, I have just been wanting to do that for so long, and I felt that this was the right moment. I hope I did not overstep."

Olivia shook her head. "No, not at all. I was just taken by surprise. I really like you, Caleb. I'm just nervous. I have never had a boyfriend before, and this is all new for me."

Caleb gave a hopeful smile, confessing, "This is new for me too. I have never had a girlfriend either. I guess we will just figure it out together."

Olivia reached out to him and pulled him into a hug.

"That sounds like a plan. See you tomorrow."

She got into her car and drove away with Caleb watching with a wistful expression on his face.

Olivia woke up at Clara's house the next morning. They had breakfast and then got ready for church. Olivia threw her long hair into a high ponytail and put on a pair of cream-colored pants with a sage-green sweater. She finished the look with a pair of brown suede ankle boots. Olivia had shared her and Caleb's thoughts on reaching more people in the community with Clara, who thought it was a wonderful idea, but was hesitant to bring Daniel into the mix.

"He's been acting so weird, plus he has been hanging out with Pete Langston and Brian Winter. They are bad news."

"What do you mean, bad news?" Olivia questioned with a frown.

"Well, they have been known to use drugs, and they drink a lot. They are big-time partiers. I think Pete actually was arrested for breaking into an elderly woman's home last year and stealing some of her jewelry. Daniel seems to have changed these past couple of months, and he rarely comes to church anymore."

"Well, you have known him a lot longer than I have. I still think we should try to involve him. Maybe we can convince him to stop hanging out with those guys."

Clara agreed, "You are right. We should try to reach as many people as we can. Jesus would not give up on him, and we should not either."

After church Caleb rounded up Olivia, Clara, Marty, Emma, and Seth. Caleb had tried calling Daniel, who had not shown up again for church, but the call went right to voice mail. They went downstairs to the recreation room to strategize how to reach more people in their community.

Caleb started their meeting, "I talked to my dad last night, and he thought it might be a good idea if we organized a church cookout and invited people from the community. We could do flyers and social media posts. Dad thought that while we had them there for the cookout, we could pass out a brochure that he would create that described the tribulation. He would be in charge of the educational literature we handed out, and we would be in charge of organizing and advertising the event."

Clara clapped her hands in delight. "I love it. Not only do we get to reach more people, but I love organizing a party. This sounds like so much fun."

Emma looked somewhat doubtful, saying, "It sounds like a lot of work to me. When we go back to school, I am sure I will be hit with a ton of homework."

Seth shook his head, suggesting, "If we all divided it up, it should not be too much work. Everyone can have a job, or we can work in pairs. I think it will be fun."

Olivia agreed, "I love the idea. When does your dad think we should do this? It seems a little cold right now to have a barbeque."

"Dad thought we could plan to have the cookout the first week of April. That will give us enough time to organize it, and the weather should be good. He recommended that we ask for donations from some of the businesses for food and money. He also thought we could do some gift baskets and have a drawing for them. The money we collect can help anyone that will need assistance with preparing for the upcoming food shortage."

"I'm in. I will help with whatever you need. Just don't ask me to ask for donations. I hate that kind of stuff," Marty said with a grimace.

Emma agreed that with everyone helping, it should be do-able and not overwhelming. She added, "If I get behind in my schoolwork, I'm going to have to back out."

"Deal. We want this to be fun and not feel like a chore," Caleb responded.

They decided to have the cookout on April 4 as it was the Saturday before Easter Sunday, and the group felt this would be a good day to celebrate. Once they decided on the date, they spent the rest of the morning dividing up tasks and coming up with a game plan as to how to advertise the event. They all went home that afternoon feeling satisfied with the progress they had made.

## Chapter Thirteen

Good Friday, April 3, 2026

The last few months had flown by. Matt had his thirteenth birthday on February 23. He wanted to go bowling, so the three of them, along with his friend Mark, went out to dinner, and then they went to Blairsville Galaxy Bowling. Elizabeth was the top bowler that night and spent the rest of the evening bragging about her win. Olivia was just happy to see her mom and brother laughing and joking like in the old times.

Olivia and her friends had met weekly after church to organize the church cookout for Saturday. Pastor Thomas had made up brochures detailing the events of the tribulation. Clara was in charge of social media posts and advertising the events. Seth and Emma worked together to get businesses to donate food, money, as well as gift baskets to raffle at the event. They also were able to get a bounce house, some carnival games, and pony rides for the event. Olivia and Caleb were in charge of overseeing the cookout and had convinced Jeff from their church to DJ the party.

That Friday morning before the event, the group gathered together at church to go over last-minute details. The girls were organizing a silent auction for the donated gift baskets while Caleb and Seth were setting up tables outside to put the food and drinks.

The girls were laughing and joking while listening to contemporary Christian music on the radio. Clara would spontaneously break out singing and dancing around the room, while the rest would not bother to hide their amusement at Clara's obvious lack of coordination and tone deafness.

While they were setting the baskets out with their coordinating sign-up sheets, the music stopped, and there was a breaking news broadcast. Olivia, instantly on alert, shushed the girls in order to hear the report.

The newscaster reported that recurring terrorist attacks by Pakistan-sponsored militant groups had led to threats of military retaliation by India. India had sent troops into Pakistan who was threatening to use nuclear weapons to counterbalance India's superior military forces. Relations between the two countries deteriorated since India had withdrawn the special status of Jammu and Kashmir and bifurcated the state into two union territories in August 2019.

When the newscaster finished, they all looked at each other with grim expressions.

Olivia was the first to break the silence, "Do you think this is the war that we have been anticipating?"

Clara shrugged her shoulders, replying, "Could be. It is so hard to say…but it does fit the timeline. They have not actually gone to war yet, but it sounds like they are leading up to it."

"Well, at least it is way over in the Mideast and not here. That was my biggest fear," Marty added with a grimace.

"What's going on? You all look so serious," Caleb questioned as he and Seth walked into the rec room.

Olivia filled them in as to what they heard on the radio. "What do you think, Caleb? Is this the war we have been waiting for?"

"I really don't know, but even if it is not now, it will be soon. I would rather it happen far away from us than in our backyard."

Marty laughed, sharing, "That's what I said. Not that I want war, but can you imagine if it was here, in the United States."

Clara raised her eyebrows and said, "I feel bad for all the people over in Europe and the Middle East. It seems they are always at war. I can't imagine living like that.

"I am so glad we are having this cookout tomorrow, which will give us a chance to try and reach more people. Well, at least tell them what is going on. I feel we are least trying," Olivia said hopefully.

They continued to work on setting up for the cookout late into the afternoon. When they were finished, they walked to Blue Jeans Pizza and Pasta and had a late lunch. The group talked excitedly about the party tomorrow and were hoping for a good turnout. The weather was expected to be warm in the low seventies and sunny.

Once they were done eating, they all said their goodbyes, and Olivia headed home. When she pulled into the driveway, she noticed her neighbors, Susan and Tyler, were outside playing with the kids. She walked over to their driveway and watched as Tyler was helping Cooper learn to ride a bike without training wheels; Susan and Peyton were cheering him on.

Olivia experienced a moment of sadness, as she remembered back when her dad taught her to ride her bicycle and how patient he was. She recalled that feeling of safety when he was holding on and how she did not want him to let go. How she wished she could have those times back with him! Olivia was having a hard time even remembering what his voice sounded like.

She quickly shook off her sorrow and went over to the Webbers to say hello.

"Hey, guys. Looks like you are having a fun time," she said cheerfully.

"It's bittersweet. You love to see your kids reach their milestones, but it is also sad to see them grow up and not need you as much," Susan responded with a grim smile.

Olivia nodded in agreement and said, "I just wanted to let you all know that my church is having a cookout tomorrow. We will be having kid games, a silent auction, and of course, lots of food. It would be great if you guys were able to come."

Tyler turned from holding onto Cooper's bike and said, "That sounds like fun. We are always looking for something to do with the kids that is family-oriented. What time does it start?"

"We open at 11:00 a.m., and it goes until 2:00 p.m. We even have pony rides," Olivia said with a bright smile.

"I want to ride a pony!" Peyton yelled out.

Tyler laughed, consenting, "Well, I guess that answers the question. We will definitely be there. Thanks for the invite, Olivia." He looked at her with concern, "How are you guys doing? We don't see much of you."

"We are actually doing very well. It took time to get adjusted, but I really like living here, and I have made some good friends."

"That's wonderful. Don't forget: if you ever need anything, we are right next door," Tyler responded reassuringly.

"Well, I better get inside before Mom sends a search party. I will see you tomorrow," Olivia yelled as she walked to her front door.

Olivia found her mom watching the news on TV in the living room. Olivia sat next to her on the couch and gave her a quick side hug. "What's going on, Mom?"

"Just watching the news about a potential war between Pakistan and India. How are you? Did you get all the preparation done for tomorrow?" her mom asked.

"Yes, everything is ready. I'm really looking forward to this. I saw Susan and Tyler outside and invited them."

"Oh, good. I have been meaning too, but it seems like I never see them," her mom responded.

"Clara, Seth, and Emma have been inviting everyone in town, and Clara has been sending out social-media blasts all month…so we should have a good turnout," Olivia said hopefully.

Elizabeth reached over and gave Olivia a hug.

"I am so proud of all of you. This was a great idea, and if we can just reach a couple of people, we are doing well."

"Thanks, Mom. I really feel good about this. I'm going to go upstairs and give Kylie a call. It's been a while, and I would still like to tell her what's going on."

"Okay, dinner will not be ready for a couple more hours. I wasn't sure what time you were coming home, so I told Matt we would eat around seven."

"Where is Matt, by the way?" Olivia questioned.

"He's over at his friend Brian's house. I have to pick him up at six thirty unless you want to."

"Sure. Text me his address," Olivia agreed. "I will be upstairs."

Olivia ran upstairs and flopped onto her bed. She pulled out her cell phone to FaceTime Kylie. To her surprise, she picked up immediately.

"Hey, Olivia."

"Oh my gosh, Kylie, I can't believe I am actually talking to you. It seems like forever. How are you?"

"Okay. We moved to this tiny town in New York, where it is freezing, and there are no stores around anywhere," Kylie complained.

"When did that happen?" Olivia asked sympathetically.

"Just after Christmas. They sold my house and pretty much everything in it. The house we moved into is like a hundred years old and drafty. I don't know anyone. The girls are very cliquish, and there are absolutely no cute guys here. They all work on farms and have dirt under their nails," Kylie whined.

"I'm so sorry, Kylie. Why didn't you call me? I remember how hard it was to move to Georgia, but I have to say it is much better now. I have made some good friends, and things are going much better. I actually have a boyfriend, I think," Olivia said with a chuckle.

"I don't think I will ever be happy again. My life is ruined. The good news is I can do what I want when I am eighteen, which is only a year away. Sara and Mike put the money from the sale of the house and all the life insurance from my parents in a trust, which I can have when I am eighteen."

"What are your plans at that time? Do you still plan to go to the University of South Florida for early childhood education?" Olivia asked.

"I'm not sure. I just know I need to get out of this Podunk town. I will probably go back to Florida and start college, or I might take a year off. I have been talking with Rachel, and we will probably move in together after high school."

Olivia was surprised. All Kylie had ever talked about was going away to college and becoming a teacher, as her mother had been.

"It sounds like you have been going through a lot. Maybe this summer you can visit me for a week or two. I would love to show you around: there are some cool waterfalls here," Olivia offered.

Kylie took a moment to answer, and when she did, she sounded unsure, "That sounds great. Let me talk to Mike and Sarah, and I will let you know. They have been really weird lately. Sarah has gotten religious and keeps talking about the end of the world. She tries to convince me that we are going through the tribulation right now, but I really think she has just lost her mind with all that has happened."

"That's funny that you brought up the tribulation because I have had it in my mind to talk to you about what is happening in the world."

Olivia went on to explain to Kylie what she had learned in her meetings with Pastor Thomas and their plans for tomorrow's cook-out. Kylie just sat and listened and did not say a word until Olivia asked at the end, "What are you thinking? You were awfully quiet."

"I'm really not sure what to think. Sarah has been saying the same thing for the past six months, and now you are pretty much confirming what she has said. Either you all are crazy, or maybe there is some truth to it."

Kylie sounded confused. Olivia felt bad for her. Kylie had gone to a Christian school with her, but her parents were not religious. Her parents had never taken her to church or read the Bible to her. This was probably all pretty foreign to her.

"I have to go, Olivia, but I will let you know about this summer. Have fun tomorrow at your cookout."

After they hung up, Olivia lay in her bed, glad she was finally able to speak to Kylie about the tribulation but also worried that she was not taking it seriously. What she had not asked Kylie was if she accepted Jesus as her Savior, as that is the only way into heaven.

Olivia realized she had a missed text and saw that her mom had sent her the address to Brian's, Matt's friend, house. Looking at her clock, she realized if she did not leave now, she would be late.

# Chapter Fourteen

## Saturday, April 4, 2026

The day of the cookout finally arrived. Olivia and her friends were at the church at 9:00 a.m. to set everything up. The food vendors, bounce house, and pony rides would arrive at 10:30 a.m.

By 10:45 a.m., people were arriving. Olivia was surprised at the crowd waiting in line to get into the church. The activities were set up in the outside courtyard of the church with access only through the church.

Pastor Thomas and some of the other members of the church were handing out brochures as people walked in. Emma, Marty, and Seth were spread out throughout the courtyard, ensuring that all of the activities were staffed by volunteers from the church. Clara and Olivia were in charge of food, and Caleb was overseeing the silent auction.

Olivia recognized several people from town at the event, as well as her neighbors, Susan and Tyler. Olivia smiled as she noticed them come in, and Peyton immediately ran to the pony rides. Millie and Austin had also shown up with their two little girls.

The event ran very smoothly; the large courtyard was packed. DJ Jeff had several people out on the dance floor. Olivia was worried they would run out of food, but thankfully, they had been well prepared.

Pastor Thomas had interrupted the music halfway through the celebration to speak to the crowd.

"Thank you all for coming out today. I want to thank my son, Caleb, and his friends, Olivia, Clara, Emma, Marty, and Seth, for organizing this event. The idea came to them as a result of meetings we have been having at the church. They recognized that they were not reaching enough people to let them know about Jesus. They came up with this idea to spread the news of not only Jesus but how the events of today are indicators that we are in the midst of the Great Tribulation." Pastor Thomas held up the brochure. "I have handed out information material as you came in, and I recommend that you look this over. Today, I would just like to take the time to spread the word of Jesus. I'm not going to bore you all with a long sermon," he said with a smile. "That is not why you are here today. I would like you to know that John said it the best in 3:16. 'For God so loved the world, that he gave his only Son, that whoever believes in him should not perish but have eternal life.'[6] We are in troubled times right now. I would like to see you all have eternal life, but without Jesus, it is not possible."

Pastor Thomas paused and looked out into the crowd.

"Many of you are from the church, but there are also several here that do not normally come to Sunday service. I would like to invite all of you to come out this Sunday. We will be doing baptisms after the 9:00 a.m. and 11:00 a.m. services. Jesus said, 'Truly, truly, I say to you, unless one is born of water and the Spirit, he cannot enter into the kingdom of God.'[7] I will also be talking more about the tribulation and what we can do to prepare. Everyone is welcome. If you are interested in baptism, please let me know. I won't keep you any longer, have a good time."

While Pastor Thomas was speaking, Olivia had a light-bulb moment. She realized that she was focused on the tribulation, but what she should have been focusing on was Jesus and spreading the word of him. She vowed to make more of a concerted effort to tell people about Jesus. Olivia had been taught from the time she was a young child that no one comes to the Father except through Jesus, and she assumed that everyone knew that. It did not occur to her that many people did not grow up in church or reading the Bible, and they were at risk for not going to heaven.

At that moment, Olivia heard a voice in her head telling her that she was duty-bound to preach the gospel of Jesus Christ. She looked around to make sure no one was talking to her, but she was standing alone; Caleb had walked over to his dad and was talking with him. She smiled to herself and walked over to Clara to see how the food was holding up.

Close to the end of the event, Pastor Thomas had stopped over to where Caleb and Olivia were standing watching the activities.

"This is going really well. I ran out of brochures to hand out; thank goodness it seems that it is winding down," Pastor Thomas said with a smile.

"I think the whole town showed up. How did people respond to the pamphlet and the news regarding the tribulation?" Caleb asked.

"Well, it was a mixed response. Some seemed very interested and indicated that they would either come to church tomorrow or would start coming to the meetings. Others just took the pamphlet and walked off. I have a feeling I will find many of them in the garbage," Pastor Thomas said with a chuckle. "That's okay, though. Our goal was to reach as many people as possible. We did not expect to convert everyone."

Olivia nodded in agreement and said, "I am just glad we did this. It was actually fun organizing the event and seeing so many people having a good time. I think we should make it an annual event."

"Well, if the prophecy is correct, we only have about two more cookouts before the last half of the tribulation," Caleb said dryly.

"Oh yeah, I keep forgetting about that," Olivia said with a sad smile.

Caleb pulled her into a hug. "I wish I could," he whispered into her ear.

Olivia warmed at the sweet gesture and hugged him back but was quickly interrupted by Clive, a member of their church, who ran up to Pastor Thomas with an agitated expression on his face.

"Did you hear the news?"

"What news?"

The look on Pastor Thomas's face gave away that he had no idea what Clive was talking about.

"Pakistan just deployed over 150 nuclear weapons on India. They hit the major cities, their army, and air bases, as well as their submarine fleet."

Olivia, Caleb, and Pastor Thomas just stood there in shock. Olivia's stomach felt sick with nerves. She looked over at Caleb, who had a horrified expression on his face.

Pastor Thomas was the first to respond, "When did this happen?"

Clive shook his head, replying, "I'm not sure, but I am assuming within the last hour. I heard it on the radio as I was headed over here to help clean up."

Pastor Thomas sighed.

"Okay, well, let's not say anything else to anyone at this time. It's after 2:00 p.m., so we will start cleaning up, and I guess we can figure out what the next steps will be after that."

Olivia and Caleb rounded up the rest of the teens, and they spent the next two hours cleaning up from the cookout. Elizabeth and Matthew stayed behind and helped. Once they were finished, they all met in the sanctuary to discuss the recent events.

They all pulled their phones out and started looking at the news report.

From what Olivia and the rest could determine, Pakistan had received intel that India had begun assembling and readying their nuclear weapons, whether true or not; Pakistan retaliated and launched a full-scale nuclear war with them. The prime minister of India was spared, as he was rushed to an underground nuclear bunker.

India apparently was in a nuclear-ready state and was able to fire back within fifteen minutes. They attacked the major cities of Pakistan, including Karachi, Lahore, Faisalabad, and Rawalpindi. They also hit the three major seaports: Karachi Port, Muhammad Bin Qasim port, and Gwadar Port, as well as Pakistani air-force bases in Sargodha, Peshawar, and Quetta.

Pakistan had attacked Mumbai, New Delhi, Kolkata, Chennai, Pune, Hyderabad, the army bases in Ahmedabad and Kolkata, their air bases in Punjab and Rajasthan, as well as their submarine fleet in Visakhapatnam and Mumbai.

The major news outlets were anticipating that the immediate effects of the bombs would kill approximately twenty-six million in India and eighteen million in Pakistan. Moreover, these projected body counts did not take into consideration the secondary effects of nuclear blasts. They reported that many survivors of the initial explosion would suffer from radiation exposure, which can cause a slow, lingering death.

What was most terrifying to the group, as they were reading and discussing their findings, was that war would threaten not only the locations where bombs were targeted but the entire world. The number of casualties was estimated to be as many as 125 million people, which was more than the death toll during all six years of World War II.

The nuclear-ignited fires released black carbon in smoke, which would spread globally within weeks. In the weeks and months after the explosions, a global climate catastrophe could follow, triggering mass starvation as crops would fail across the planet.

The newscasters were reporting, "This is a war that would have no precedent in human experience. We could have a nuclear winter." The long-term health effects of the exposure could last decades, and global weather patterns could be impacted for the next twenty-five years.

One article was particularly alarming to the group, the report indicated that particles from the nuclear blasts would block out light from the sun, causing surface temperatures to decrease, which would shorten growing seasons by ten to forty days, and certain crops would simply become unviable. They anticipated that global agricultural yields would fall, leading to rising prices and famine. A global economic recession was expected.

"So much for a war over in the Middle East not affecting us," Marty said dryly.

"Well, we knew that this was coming. We are planning for a famine…that was one of the reasons we held the barbecue to raise money to help out those that could not afford to store food for the next couple of years," Caleb responded matter-of-factly.

Olivia nodded in agreement. "I am glad we have been buying and storing items for the past several months. Our basement is totally full of bottled water, canned goods, and toilet paper. I think my mom thinks there is going to be a toilet-paper shortage like when Covid first hit the US," she said with a smile.

Marty laughed out loud, sharing, "My dad's also buying up all kinds of paper goods. I think we all have post-traumatic stress from Covid."

Pastor Thomas interrupted their reminiscing over the last pandemic by noting that the church had a large hoard of food and supplies: "I would like to keep that for those that are in need. Hopefully, the church families will have taken heed to my sermon in January about preparing for a famine."

Everyone in the sanctuary reassured him that they had been storing up since that time. Pastor Thomas reassured the group that he planned to focus on the upcoming famine, as well as accepting Jesus as their Lord and Savior in the sermon tomorrow.

Olivia looked around at her friends and the other adults. They all had a look of nervous excitement on their face as if they were almost looking forward to the next cataclysmic event to happen. Olivia herself was terrified of what would happen next.

## Chapter Fifteen

When the Lamb opened the third seal, I heard the third living creature say, "Come!" I looked, and there before me was a black horse! Its rider was holding a pair of scales in his hand.

*Revelation 6:5*

### August 2, 2026

Olivia had woken up to her mother and brother singing "Happy Birthday" to her. Elizabeth was smiling brightly while carrying the bed tray filled with Olivia's favorites, chocolate chip pancakes, raspberries, and chocolate milk. Olivia was happy that no matter what was going on in the world, her mother still attempted to make life seem normal.

The last few months had been chaotic throughout the world. Marcus Aldric immediately called a meeting of the World Union following the nuclear war between Pakistan and India. Mr. Aldric was able to broker a temporary peace agreement between the two countries. Given the anticipated state of the world economy, the World Union had met with all the major leaders of the world and had enacted a centralized government for the foreseeable future. Mr. Aldric was appointed as the leader of the World Union temporarily until a vote could be undertaken. They created a council of leaders from the ten most influential countries in the world, which included the United States, the United Kingdom, Russia, Germany, France, China, Japan, Italy, Israel, and Saudi Arabia. They divided the other countries up throughout the world, and they each were assigned to one of the ten major countries. The council of leaders would meet separately with the leaders from their assigned countries to discuss the issues and form one vote that would then be brought to the World Union.

Marcus Aldric held a press meeting and spoke of all the advantages of a centralized world government. He claimed that the World Union would be able to deal with horrendous acts, such as the nuclear war between Pakistan and India, swiftly. Mr. Aldric noted that there would be increased efficiency in business with standardized regulations across the world, countries would be able to combine technologies, there would be open travel/migration, standardized environmental and judicial laws, improved capability to build up third-world countries and fight famine. Mr. Aldric reported that the World Union was working on a standardized currency that would be a form of cryptocurrency.

The world, devastated by the events in April, was all willing and accepting of the new centralized government. The United States had fallen into a recession, and the economy throughout the world was failing. Refugees from Pakistan and India were flooding into Afghanistan, Iran, Nepal, and Bangladesh. These poor states were struggling to support the millions of refugees.

Immediately following the nuclear blasts, thick black clouds blocked out all but a fraction of the sun's light for several weeks, which cooled the earth's temperature by almost five degrees. Concern for shortened growing seasons and even unviable crops led to rising prices and worsening famine across the world as global agricultural yields were falling.

Scientists were concerned that the particles would deplete twenty to thirty percent of the ozone layer, which would allow more of the sun's radiation to penetrate the atmosphere. The long-term effects would be increased rates of skin cancer, as well as killing off sensitive plant life and marine plankton, which could decimate the sea life.

Many survivors of the initial explosion were suffering slow, lingering deaths due to radiation exposure. Several countries were seeing a collapse in healthcare, sanitation, and clean water. Wealthier citizens, numbering in tens of millions, were using their resources to flee abroad.

The world was looking for answers and saw Marcus Aldric as their protector and savior. He had stopped Pakistan and India from continuing with their war, which, if it had continued, would have potentially destroyed the planet. The world was in chaos, and many of the leaders did not know how to remedy the situation, so they were happy to give up control to the World Union.

Olivia and her family had not suffered much from the fallout. Elizabeth quit her job at the hospital. She had spent little of the money that she had received from the life insurance on her husband and from the sale of their home in Florida. She felt it was more important to spend her time with Olivia and Matthew and also help out where she could in the community. Olivia's grandparents, Sandy and Gene, came to visit over the summer. They were devoted Christians and were prepared for the end of the world. Sandy joked that it was about time. She had been waiting years for it to happen. Gene was more serious about it and was anxious to return to their home in Pennsylvania to start preparing.

After the church's barbecue in April, Pastor Thomas saw a surge in church membership. Several people had been baptized since that time. Olivia and her friends spent the summer working with the church to hand out food to those that needed it and take the opportunity to continue to preach about Jesus. Daniel had been pretty much MIA during the summer. Clara had expressed her concerns to Olivia that he was definitely mixed up with the wrong crowd and that she was concerned about him. Caleb continued to try and reach out to him, to no avail, but he stated he would not give up.

Once Olivia was finished with breakfast, she carried the tray downstairs. Her mother was washing dishes in the kitchen. Olivia set the tray on the counter and placed the dishes in the sink.

"How was breakfast?" Elizabeth asked.

"Wonderful as usual. Thanks so much, Mom. I do appreciate you," Olivia said with a smile as she reached over to her mother and gave her a big hug.

"What are your plans for the rest of the day?" her mother asked.

"Well, Caleb is taking me out for lunch. Hopefully, I will be hungry by then. I think he said 1:00 p.m. I better text him to be sure. That gives me about four hours to digest my breakfast," Olivia said with a grin.

"That sounds like fun. I do have some presents for you to open. Do you want to open them now or later?"

"What do you think, Mom? Now, of course."

"All right. They are in the living room on the coffee table."

Olivia raced into the living room and noticed a pile of presents on the table. Elizabeth yelled after her, "Wait for me before you open them!" She then yelled upstairs, "Matt, come down here; Olivia is going to open her presents!"

Olivia sighed loudly and yelled, "Matt, hurry up; don't take all day!"

Both Matthew and Elizabeth walked into the living room a few seconds later. Olivia immediately began unwrapping the first present, which was a small box. Inside the box was a charm bracelet with three gold charms. One was a cross, the other a Bible, and the third was an angel.

"Oh, Mom, this is so pretty. Thank you so much. I love it," Olivia exclaimed.

"I wanted to get something for you that was sentimental, versus just getting you clothes as usual. I'm glad you like it. The nice part is we can add charms to it as special events happen."

Olivia gave her mother another hug.

"It's perfect, thanks."

She quickly unwrapped the other presents, which consisted of several shirts, jeans, and a couple of skirts from her favorite online clothing store that Olivia had asked for. Matthew had gotten her some candles and body wash.

After she was finished unwrapping her presents, she sat back on the couch and thought how lucky she was. A year ago, she would never have thought she would be this happy again. Even with the upcoming events of the tribulation looming overhead, she still was able to find joy in her life.

Caleb came right at 1:00 p.m. to pick her up for lunch. He had also brought a present. Olivia waited until they were alone in the restaurant to open it. The box was beautifully wrapped in gold foil paper and had a small silver bow on top. She gently unwrapped the gift and found it was another charm to go on her bracelet. Caleb had gotten her a gold heart with their initials on it.

"Your mom told me she was getting a charm bracelet, so I thought this would be a perfect gift to go with it." Caleb appeared unsure of himself.

"It is perfect. Thank you so much. I wish I had worn the bracelet to lunch so I could put the charm on," Olivia reassured him with a genuine smile. She got up from her chair, walked around the table, and gave him a hug. At that moment, Olivia thought life was pretty perfect, and she wished it would stay that way.

Olivia and Caleb finished lunch, and he drove her back home. He helped her put the new charm on her bracelet, and they decided to play some video games with Matthew, who was thrilled. Olivia had invited her friends to come over later to celebrate her birthday. Clara, Emma, Seth, and Marty arrived around 4:00 p.m. Elizabeth drove into town and picked up pizza, wings, as well as cake and ice cream for them to celebrate.

Marty and Clara had arranged to spend the night. Emma had work in the morning, so she decided not to stay and left when Caleb and Seth did, around 11:00 p.m. The girls stayed up late, gossiping and watching reruns of *Friends* on TV. None of them brought up or discussed the tribulation, and for one night, they were able to pretend everything was going to be all right.

## Chapter Sixteen

### March 28, 2027

"Breakfast is ready," Elizabeth yelled upstairs.

Olivia groaned as she rolled out of bed: it was Sunday; why did she have to get up so early to have breakfast? They usually went to the 11:00 a.m. church service, but Elizabeth wanted to go to the 9:00 a.m. service this morning, as it was Easter, and was making a big dinner later.

Olivia heard Matthew clomping down the stairs. She figured she might as well get up and join her family. She had showered last night, so it would not take long for her to get ready for church.

Her mother had a full spread of food on the counter when she arrived in the kitchen. "Wow, Mom, this looks great!"

Matthew nodded in agreement and grabbed a piece of bacon off the plate. They piled their plates full and sat at the kitchen table to eat.

Olivia looked pensive and said, "I can't believe it is already Easter. This school year has flown by."

"I know! You will be graduating in two months. I can't believe that is even possible," Elizabeth mused. "Have you decided what you want to do afterward?"

Olivia chewed on her bottom lip.

"No idea. As you know, I was accepted into the University of North Georgia, I think I will go with them as their online program appears quite comprehensive, but I'm keeping my options open at this time."

"I'm glad you are staying home. I would be a nervous wreck if you went away to college." Her mom appeared relieved with her choice.

"I was hoping you would go away so I could have your bedroom; it's bigger than mine," Matthew interjected.

"Ha ha, you know you would miss me!" Olivia said teasingly.

"Have you heard from Emma or Daniel since they went away?"

Emma and Daniel had both graduated in June of last year. Emma's parents' divorce was finalized over the summer, and Emma and Seth's mother moved back to New Jersey, where she had family. Emma had decided to put off going to college and stayed in Blue Ridge until after Thanksgiving, when she decided to move to New Jersey with her mom. Seth chose to stay in Georgia with his father, as he had returned to school in the fall as a junior. He wanted to finish out school at Fannin County High School. Olivia had heard that Daniel had moved to Atlanta to go to college. They had not spoken with him since earlier in the year. She often thought of him and hoped he was doing okay.

"I talk to Emma once in a while. She is doing okay at her mom's house. I am kinda worried about her, though. Her mom did not go to church, and I think she is having a negative effect on Emma," Olivia said grimly. "Seth says his mom is somewhat of a flower child and was pretty much antireligious when they were growing up. That was one of the reasons their parents divorced, over religious views. You know their dad; he is an active member of the church and has been very vocal about his beliefs in Jesus."

"Well, hopefully, Emma has a good enough foundation from her years with her dad to not be too swayed by her mother's viewpoint," Elizabeth responded as she stood up and started grabbing plates.

"All right, I'm going to clean up the kitchen while you two get ready for church. We will leave in twenty minutes."

"I better get going then," Olivia stated as she jumped up from her chair and ran upstairs. She heard Matthew right behind her.

The Ahrens arrived at church right before 9:00 a.m. Olivia had chosen to wear a sleeveless halter maxi sundress with a muted tropical print in soft pastel colors. She added a white cardigan sweater to wear over it, as mornings were very cool in north Georgia in March. This morning it was only thirty-four degrees.

Olivia quickly found her friends in their usual pew. She gestured for Matthew and Elizabeth to follow her as she walked up to where they were sitting. Marty moved over so Olivia could sit next to Caleb. He reached out and grabbed her hand and gave it a squeeze as she smiled up at him.

The choir sang for fifteen minutes, and then Pastor Thomas started the service with prayer. The message for the day was about the way to heaven, and he concentrated on the chapter of John.

"When Jesus spoke to His disciples before His crucifixion, He reassured them that He would return and take them with Him. When Thomas questioned where He was going and how they could know the way, Jesus answered, 'I am the way and the truth and the life. No one comes to the Father except through me. If you really know me, you will know my Father as well. From now on, you do know him and have seen him.'8" Pastor Thomas paused for dramatic effect and then continued, "There is only one way to heaven, my friends, and that is through Jesus. He sacrificed His life that we may all have eternal life if we choose."

Pastor Thomas stared out at the large crowd in the church.

"I hope that you all have chosen to have the Lord Jesus Christ as your Savior. Do you believe in Him and trust that He will take away your sin and make you right before God? If you do, then you will have a home in heaven. At this moment, Jesus is preparing our homes for us, and I don't know about the rest of you, but I am ready for my mansion in the sky."

The crowd in the church all enthusiastically yelled out, "Amen!"

After church, Olivia and her friends stood around talking for a while. Elizabeth had planned a traditional Easter dinner and had invited all of Olivia's friends, as well as their parents, to come over. Marty's mom was not feeling well and did not come to church, so Marty and her dad passed on dinner. Clara had told Olivia that Marty's mom was on hospice now and probably would only last another month or two. Marty did not talk about it very much, and Olivia did not usually bring it up, as she did not want to upset her.

Dinner was a festive affair. Elizabeth had set the table with her good china, a pink-lace tablecloth and had place card settings for everyone. They all ate until they were stuffed, and after dinner, they played Pictionary. It was a fun afternoon, and when everyone left, Elizabeth remarked, "I am so happy that we decided to go to that first church meeting almost two years ago. We have really met some wonderful people through the Blue Ridge Methodist Church."

"I agree, Mom. What if you had decided not to go? I wonder if I would have any friends here," Olivia pondered.

Matt, who rarely commented on his social life, agreed, "I'm glad you met with Pastor Thomas that day downtown. I really feel like this is my home now. I still miss Dad and Katie, but there really is still a lot of good in our lives."

"Wow, Matt, that is the first time I have heard you say anything nice about Blue Ridge," Olivia exclaimed.

"I am just so pleased that the both of you are happy and that we have created a new life for ourselves here. I know that it is only temporary, but we can enjoy the time we are still on this earth," Elizabeth said with a smile.

Olivia and her mom watched the evening news while Matthew was playing computer games in his room. The newscasters were pretty bleak when discussing the events occurring in the world. The World Union was taking quick action to put everything in place to centralize the governments. There were news reports every day of countries suffering from starvation. There were many who had stockpiled items and who were now selling them at inflated prices to others who had not been so well prepared. The World Union had put into place a new form of cryptocurrency called Terra-Cash, which was being regulated through the World Bank. It was accepted in all countries, and there was no need to worry about exchange rates. Cash was no longer an option.

At the end of the nightly news, the newscaster, Ryan Scott, announced that he would be ending the show on a positive note. The World Council of Religious Leaders with Allesandro D'Angelo at the helm had broadcast a live service from Rome. His official title was now Prophet D'Angelo. The service was the most-watched televised event in history, with over a billion viewers. According to Ryan, the focus of the service was on unity and supporting the World Union leaders in bringing the world together to fight off hunger, disease, and racism. He condemned nationalism and encouraged all nations to welcome immigrants to their country, as people were now under the one-world government. Ryan reported that the response was positive and more people were feeling encouraged about the future since hearing the broadcast.

Olivia and her mother watched excerpts from Prophet D'Angelo's service, and she could understand why many would be taken in by him. He was an eloquent speaker and very debonair. He appeared sincere, but Olivia and Elizabeth knew better. It was scary to watch him and to know that this was the false prophet that the Bible had prophesized.

# Chapter Seventeen

## May 28, 2027

Graduation day finally arrived. Olivia had anticipated this day for years and now felt it was anticlimactic. She had always pictured graduating with the kids she had gone to school with at Sarasota Christian School since kindergarten. She had imagined them all together, taking pictures and then going from one party to the next in celebration. She and Kylie had even planned to have a joint party at Olivia's house. Following graduation, they had planned to go to college together and then eventually share an apartment. She never imagined that her graduation day would be with virtual strangers, except for Caleb and Clara. She knew a few from church but did not have a close relationship with any of them.

Graduation was scheduled for 8:00 p.m. at the high-school stadium. Caleb was scheduled to pick Olivia up at 7:00 p.m., as they had to be at the school by 7:30. She spent the day going through some of her pictures and mementos from school and her years in Sarasota.

Elizabeth walked to her room to let her know lunch was ready, and she found Olivia teary-eyed, looking at pictures of the family on their last vacation to Colorado. They all looked so happy in the pictures.

"That seems a lifetime ago," Elizabeth remarked.

"I know, I feel guilty sometimes that I am happy, and then I look at these pictures and wish our life could go back to the way it was," Olivia said tearfully.

"Your happiness should never be at the expense of someone or something else. You deserve to have joy in your life. There is always going to be sadness, death, and loss. We need to just look for joy in everyday life. Your father and sister would not want you to wallow in misery for the rest of your life. They would want you to be happy. Do not feel guilty about that. Your father loved you more than anything. He would never have wanted to see you sad and miserable," Elizabeth said emphatically as she pulled Olivia into a hug.

Olivia did not respond right away and allowed herself to be enveloped in her mother's loving embrace. She finally drew back and said tentatively, "I just wish that they were here to see me graduate. There are so many milestones in my life that they will never be part of."

"Just remember Jesus has a plan for all of us. It will not be long before we are with your father and sister again. We really just have to persevere and get through these next couple of years and continue to focus on Jesus," Elizabeth said hopefully. "Now, lunch is ready, so come on downstairs and eat. We will not have dinner until after the graduation, so you better fill up now," she said jokingly.

"Sounds good. I'll be right down. I'm just so lucky I have you and Matt. Just don't tell him I said that," Olivia said with a smile.

"It's our little secret! Don't take too long," Elizabeth replied as she walked to Matt's room to let him know lunch was ready.

The day passed by slowly. Olivia was ready to go when Caleb picked her up. She had worn a blush-colored sleeveless dress with a sweetheart neckline and a double row waist cutout. The dress had a full skirt that came just above her knees. Olivia wore her long hair loose with soft beachy waves.

Caleb gave a low whistle when he saw her.

"You look fantastic!" he gasped as he pulled her into a hug.

"You look pretty good yourself," Olivia remarked as she eyed Caleb with an appreciative look. He wore black pants and a pale-blue button-down shirt with a black-and-blue tie. His black hair was combed neatly back, which was different than his usual messy look with his hair flopping over his face.

Olivia and Caleb had picked up their caps and gowns the week prior during graduation rehearsal. They both graduated with honors, so they had special sashes to wear. Olivia was also in the top ten of her graduating class, so her name would go on a special plaque, which would be displayed in the school. Olivia placed her gown and cap gently in the back of Caleb's car and then jumped into the passenger seat. She wasn't quite sure why she was feeling nervous. All she had to do was walk in a straight line and receive her diploma.

Her grandparents were unable to make it today, as her grandfather had not been feeling well. Her mother's sister, Shari, had planned the trip, but her airline canceled the flight at the last minute. Her aunt did not have the time to drive all the way from Pennsylvania, given the short notice. Olivia was fine with that. She was not that close with her extended family. It seemed that it had been just the three of them for so long that she really did not care if anyone else came. In her mind, it was just a formality anyway. This really did not mean anything to her. She felt like she was just doing all of this to keep up appearances, but deep down, she thought, *Why bother?* The world was coming to an end in another couple of years. She was seriously rethinking even going to college. Caleb, Clara, and she talked about spending their time ministering to others in order to ensure that as many people were prepared for the rapture as possible. They all figured that would be a better use of their time versus going to college for a degree they would never use or even finish.

When they reached the school, Caleb and Olivia walked to the stadium, where they found Clara and a few of her friends. The principal, whom Olivia had only met once, was rounding everyone up and reminding them of the directions that they had reviewed the week prior at rehearsal. Caleb and Olivia were walking in the front, as all honor students were at the head of the line. Olivia was second in line, behind Grace Abbott. As the processional music began to play, she turned and gave Caleb a little wave. He smiled and gave her a thumbs-up.

As Olivia walked toward the podium where the principal, guidance counselors, and other faculty were waiting to hand out their diplomas, an overwhelming calm came over her. She immediately felt a peace that she had not felt in a long time. She thought to herself, *I am ready for the next stage of my life. I am ready to serve God and help others find their way to Jesus.*

With this decision made, she walked excitedly to her future.

## Chapter Eighteen

When he opened the fifth seal, I saw under the altar the souls of those who had been slain because of the word of God and the testimony they had maintained. They called out in a loud voice, "How long, Sovereign Lord, holy and true, until you judge the inhabitants of the earth and avenge our blood?"

*Revelation 6:9-10*

### January 8, 2028

"Wake up, Olivia; we have to get to the church. It's almost eight!" Elizabeth spoke loudly as she shook Olivia awake.

"I'm awake already. No need to yell," Olivia said sleepily. "Why do we have to be there so early?"

"You know we start handing the food out at nine. It's not like this is new for you. One day a week, you can wake up before ten," Elizabeth said sternly.

"I have to wake up early on Sunday too!" Olivia argued.

"Okay, twice a week. The rest of the time, you can get up when you want. I'll be downstairs finishing breakfast. Be down there in ten minutes."

"All right; no need to be mean," Olivia said as she rolled out of bed. "What's for breakfast?"

"I made French toast, so hurry up. Believe it or not, Matt is already up and dressed."

"Wow, that's shocking!" Olivia raised her eyebrows in surprise.

"I know, I don't know what has gotten into him these past couple of weeks, but he has been very gung ho in helping out at the church. It is so nice to see," Elizabeth said with a smile.

"Well, he will be fifteen next month: it's about time he grew up."

"He has been through a lot, Olivia. You should give him a break. This has not been easy for either of you," Elizabeth said grimly. "Now, go get ready so we are not late."

Pastor Thomas and the members of the church continued to hold food drives and hand food out every Saturday to those in need. Olivia's, as well as her friend's families, had all been well prepared and were able to continue to assist others in need.

Due to the fallout from the nuclear war, famine was rampant across the world. Third-world countries were suffering significantly. Agricultural production was disrupted as well as distribution. The world was enduring unprecedented inflation, and with it came panic, rampant crime, looting, and ultimately starvation for many. The water supply near the nuclear blasts was affected significantly as well as marine life. Death tolls were rising, not only from famine, but wars were breaking out in the Middle East. The Muslim countries were revolting over the rebuilding of the Jewish temple. The news reports were predicting that if something was not done, the death toll would reach almost two billion. There were reports of wild animals attacking people, not only in rural areas but also in urban neighborhoods.

The two witnesses continued to prophesize at the base of the Temple Mount. They were attacked daily by protestors and religious zealots who felt they were responsible for the horrors going on in the world.

There was not much news regarding Allesandro D'Angelo or the world council. Pastor Thomas felt that they were lying low until the perfect opportunity arose for the council to assert their religious authority.

Elizabeth, Olivia, and Matt got to church right on time. There were several members already there preparing boxes of food to give out to those in need. It was a perfect time to minister to the residents of Blue Ridge. The town was lucky that so many had been well prepared thanks to Pastor Thomas's preaching prior to the famine, although there still were doubters who had not taken his advice. Pastor Thomas and the rest of the congregation never made them feel bad for the choices they had made, and he continued to welcome them with open arms.

He took every opportunity he could to preach about Jesus and the need to accept Him into their life in order to be saved from the rest of the horrors of the tribulation. Pastor Thomas was convinced that the rapture would take place at any time, and he reinforced to anyone that would listen that they needed to be ready.

Olivia had decided to put off going to college for the foreseeable future. She put all her faith in Pastor Thomas's predictions that the end was near, and she did not want to spend her time taking classes that would never amount to anything. Clara, on the other hand, decided to take a few classes online at the local college. She said it was just to keep her busy and out of trouble. Caleb chose to join his father in the church and spent much of his time going from community to community preaching the Word of God. Olivia would join them at times, but other days she and Matt would go with their mother to the nearby hospitals and preach to the patients as well as the staff.

Seth and Marty were completing their senior year. The schools had completely gone online again as they had during the COVID-19 outbreak in 2020. There was so much unrest in the world that the schools were concerned about violence as well as domestic terrorist acts.

Olivia and Caleb worked together, boxing up food and handing it out. The line today was extremely long.

When Olivia remarked on this, Caleb stated, "Some of these people have been in line since 6:00 a.m. to ensure they would get food."

"That's crazy. We always have enough, but I guess the longer the famine goes on, the more scared people are getting we will run out," Olivia said grimly.

"I'm glad Dad and I planted the garden in our house, as well as the tower gardens in the church. We continue to have fresh vegetables all year long," Caleb said gratefully.

"I thought Mom went a little overboard when she was buying canned goods last year, but I am so happy she did. We have enough not only for ourselves but to share with others."

"I know; we do too. The church also had bought a ton of stuff. I don't think Dad wants to announce that too loudly, though, because he is afraid that people may start to get scared and break into the church and try to steal items in order to ensure they have enough," Caleb said worriedly.

Olivia scowled, replying, "Wow, I never even would think that people in our community would do something like that…but you never know: when people get desperate, they do crazy things."

They continued to hand out boxes until noon. Just as they were cleaning up, Austin and Millie ran into the church. Austin said breathlessly, "I hope we are not too late. Our car broke down, and we had to wait for my stepmother to give us a ride here."

Pastor Thomas greeted them, "No problem. We have plenty. Let me get you a couple of boxes. Does your stepmother need food?"

Austin gave him a grateful look, saying, "That would be great. She is waiting with the girls in the car."

Pastor Thomas and Caleb helped load up Austin's stepmother's car. Austin had stopped coming to church with Millie last year, but for the past couple of months, he had been coming sporadically. Olivia was not sure where he stood regarding his beliefs in the tribulation. They obviously did not prepare for the famine, but recently he seemed to be more open to Pastor Thomas's suggestions.

There were several people in town who initially had been doubters, but in the past couple of months, had been attending church, as well as the monthly Saturday evening meetings. Even the Ahrens neighbors, Susan and Tyler, had started coming to church with their two children. Olivia and Elizabeth had spent a lot of time over at their home, talking to them about Jesus and the events as outlined in Revelation. At first, they both were skeptical, but as the events unfolded in the world, they quickly changed their opinion. All four of the Webbers had been baptized at Christmas. Olivia had felt a sense of pride when they were up in front of the church, declaring their love for Jesus. She knew that she played a role in their accepting of the Lord into their life.

Pastor Thomas and Caleb offered to go to Austin and Millie's home later to see if they could figure out what was going on with their car. Austin readily agreed, as he admitted he was no good with mechanical things.

Millie hugged Pastor Thomas as they were getting ready to leave.

"Thank you for everything. I know this has not been easy for you, especially with those that gave you a hard time in the beginning," she said, looking over at Austin with a sardonic grin. "You are a shining example of a true Christian, Pastor Thomas."

"I just try to glorify God in everything I do, Millie. Thank you for your kind words. Please do not hesitate to reach out to us if you need anything. We will always try to help out in any way we can."

As Caleb watched Millie and Austin drive off, he turned to his father and pulled him into a hug.

"I'm so grateful for you, Dad."

Pastor Thomas patted his back as they ended the hug.

"I'm proud of the man you have become, Caleb. Your mother would be so proud of you. I know she is up in heaven right now, preparing for us to join her."

Caleb smiled, whispering, "I can't wait."

## Chapter Nineteen

### November 23, 2028

Thanksgiving morning arrived with the world in turmoil. Pastor Thomas arranged to have dinner in the church basement and had an open invitation to anyone that wanted to come. He and Caleb were in charge of the turkeys, and everyone else was responsible for bringing a dish to pass.

Elizabeth, Olivia, and Matt went to the church midmorning to help with the preparations. They were expecting at least fifty people. Clara and her mom, as well as Seth and his dad, had also arrived early to help with setup. The basement was large, and they had room for ten large folding tables, which seated eight people each. They also set up four tables to hold food. Several people donated tablecloths, and Clara and Olivia had made centerpieces out of items they found outside, pine cones, wildflowers, and candles. The room looked very festive by the time they were finished.

Pastor Thomas had borrowed a couple of smokers, as well as grills, and was cooking the turkeys outside. Olivia and her mom had made three pumpkin pies, two cherry pies, and two apple pies. They also brought a large corn casserole, which was Olivia's favorite side dish.

Guests started arriving around 2:30 p.m.; dinner was scheduled for 3:00. Marty and her dad had shown up. It was the first time Olivia had seen Marty since her mom's funeral last month. Her mom had lasted longer than they had anticipated, but it was still very hard on Marty and her dad. Olivia had reached out to her a few times, and they talked on the phone, but she had not seen her in person since that time.

Olivia went right up to Marty and gave her a hug.

"I'm so glad to see you."

Olivia turned to Marty's dad. "How are you doing, Mr. Marsh?"

"I'm doing okay. Thanks for asking, Olivia. You guys did a great job with the rec room; it looks and smells terrific."

Olivia looked around the room.

"Thanks. Everyone has helped out. I'm sure the food will be delicious."

The room was quickly filled up with members of the church, as well as locals who had nowhere else to go for dinner. Many of the guests brought a dish to pass, but no one was turned away if they did not. Olivia was surprised when Emma came walking in. She motioned to Marty to see who had arrived and grabbed her arm to pull her over to greet Emma.

Olivia grabbed Emma and pulled her into a hug. "Seth never mentioned you were coming for Thanksgiving," Olivia squealed in delight.

"I told him to keep it secret. I wanted to surprise you all," Emma said with a smile. "I'm glad to see it worked."

"He did not say a word. I'm so happy to see you. How is everything going in New Jersey? You look fantastic. I love your new haircut."

Emma waited a second before answering, ensuring that Olivia was done asking her questions. "I'm glad to see you too. I hate New Jersey. My mother was not prepared at all for the shortage of food, so we have depended on neighbors and friends to help us out. It is so embarrassing. I have decided that I am going to stay with Dad and Seth. I can't go back there."

"Oh my gosh. That's horrible. What about your mom? Are you not worried that she will starve to death? It's happening all over, even in the United States."

"She will be fine. She always lands on her feet. I think she will actually be better off without having to worry about me," Emma said with a tight smile.

"I'm sorry. I'm glad that you are back, though. I know Seth and your dad missed you."

"I actually missed them a lot. It is good to be back home." Emma turned to Marty, who had just been standing quietly. "Oh, Marty, I was so sorry to hear about your mother. Are you doing okay?" she asked gently.

"We are good. Thanks, Emma. It is so good to see you. I'm glad you're back," Marty said softly.

"Me too. Where's everyone else?" Emma looked around the room, quickly spotting Clara at the serving table. "Never mind, I see Clara."

The three girls walked over to where Clara was helping arrange the food on the serving tables. As soon as she saw Emma, she let out a loud scream. Everyone turned to see what was going on.

Clara, like Olivia, started bombarding Emma with questions. Emma held up her hand.

"Stop! I will answer everything; just give me a few minutes. I'm starving. Why don't we sit together for dinner, and I will fill you in on everything?"

They all agreed and went to find seats so they could all sit together. Olivia saved a seat for her mom and Matt, as well as Caleb and Pastor Thomas.

At 3:00 p.m., Pastor Thomas used the microphone to get everyone's attention. "I would like to thank everyone for coming out today. I know these past few months have been very difficult, and I am sad to say they will only get worse," he said with a sigh. "I am just happy to see that we can all gather together and support each other through these trying times. Please, everyone, help yourselves. As soon as everyone is seated with their dinner, we will say grace."

The food line was set up in an organized fashion, with food on both sides of the table. The turkeys all came out beautifully browned and moist. Everyone quickly filled their plates and took a seat. Pastor Thomas said grace, and then everyone dug into their food.

Olivia was amazed at the different side dishes. She was used to her mother's Thanksgiving dinner and was pleasantly surprised to try new food. People had brought all kinds of different dishes, including macaroni and cheese, fried okra, potato salad, and many things she did not even recognize.

By the time dinner was over, everyone was stuffed. Emma had caught up with her friends, and they all made plans to get together the next day. It had traditionally been Black Friday, one of the biggest shopping days of the year following Thanksgiving, but this year all of the stores were either closed or not having a big event. Due to the hard-hitting recession, people were not able to afford to go out and spend thousands on unnecessary items when food had become a luxury item.

Olivia and her mom, as well as Clara and her mom, stayed back after dinner and helped clean up. Once they had the rec room back in the order, they all sat down on the old worn-out couches that had been in the basement since the 1990s.

Caleb let out a large sigh. "Well, I'm glad that is done. I'm exhausted from cooking all those turkeys," he said with a smile.

Olivia reached over, grabbed his hand, and gave it a squeeze. "I agree: cooking and cleaning is exhausting."

Her mom laughed out loud.

"Oh really, I wouldn't know! Although even for me, it was a long day. I'm glad you offered to do this, Tom. I think it really brought us together as a community."

"Thanks, Elizabeth. Although I feel that we are helping quite a few of the members of our congregation and the community, I just worry that there are some out there too proud to ask for help."

Seth's father, Charles, who was normally quiet, asked, "What else do you think we can do, Tom, to reach more people?"

Clara spoke up, "Why don't we take the food boxes to the town square on Saturdays after we hand out food at the church? Some people may be intimidated by coming to the church and will be more open to come to a neutral zone."

Pastor Thomas nodded in agreement.

"That's a great idea, Clara. We can also use that time to hand out the pamphlet I had made up for the spring carnival last year."

The group all agreed with the plan and arranged to start this Saturday. Charles offered his truck to transport the boxes of food, and Elizabeth planned to bring her Acadia if needed. By the time they packed up their stuff and headed home, Olivia felt really good about how the day went and about their continued work on reaching more people to let them know about Jesus.

The next day Olivia met up with Emma, Clara, Marty, Caleb, and Seth at a small Deli downtown. She had invited Matt, but he declined as his friend Mark was planning on coming over to their house later. Several of the shops downtown had closed up or had very limited hours of business. Olivia thought how sad it was to see the once-thriving downtown so deserted, especially on a day that was known for being very busy.

Olivia and her family did not usually shop on Black Friday, so it was no big deal for her, but Emma was visibly upset. She was bemoaning the fact that she and her mother used to make it an annual ritual to go out early in the morning and hit all the sales. She complained that it was another thing that was taken away from her.

Clara quickly responded, "It is easy to focus on everything we have lost and feel sorry for ourselves, but we really have to think about how much better off we are than the majority of the world. We have clean clothes, a roof over our heads, and we have food in our stomachs." She made a point to look over at Marty. "I am sorry, Emma, that you are not shopping today, but there are people out there that are literally starving to death."

Emma hung her head in shame. "I know, I'm sorry. I think I have been hanging out with my mother way too much. She only talks about how things used to be, and I think she wore off on me. I am grateful for everything, and I am glad to be back in Blue Ridge with my dad and brother. Thanks, Clara, for reminding me what a tool I have been," she said with a smile.

Clara stood up and walked around to where Emma was sitting; she bent over and gave her a hug from the side.

"That's what friends are for: to call you out when you say stupid stuff," she said with a chuckle.

The mood was instantly lightened, and they finished their lunch and paid with the new Terra-Cash system. Olivia knew that it was preparing them for future tribulations, such as having to take the mark of the beast, but she did enjoy the convenience of it. They walked around the town for a while, remarking on the changes that had taken place with the global recession. After a while, Caleb suggested they all come over to his house and hang out for the afternoon. Marty declined the invitation. She made an excuse that her dad was expecting her home. She had been very quiet through the lunch, and the rest of the group was giving her time to grieve. Olivia fully understood how she was feeling. After her dad and sister died, she did not want to be around other people for quite some time.

Olivia gave Marty a hug goodbye.

"You can call or text me anytime if you need to talk. I know what you are going through, and sometimes it is nice to talk to someone who has been through it," she suggested.

Marty nodded and said, "I will, thanks. I just need time."

"Of course. Whenever you are ready, we are all here for you," Olivia said sincerely.

"Okay, see you guys tomorrow morning at church," Marty called out as she walked to her car.

Olivia hung out at Caleb's until dark. He walked her out to her car and kissed her gently goodnight. On the drive home, Olivia enjoyed the peace and quiet. It gave her time to reflect on her day and think over how much she had to be grateful for. She almost regretted when she arrived home, as the time alone in her car really helped her appreciate what God had given her.

# CHAPTER TWENTY

Thursday, December 14, 2028

Hanukkah

Olivia woke to hear voices downstairs in the kitchen. It sounded like her mother was talking to someone. She looked at the clock and saw that it was only a few minutes after eight. She wondered who would visit so early. Olivia got out of bed, went to the bathroom, brushed her teeth, and slipped on some sweatpants and a sweatshirt. The room was freezing this morning. On days like this, she missed Sarasota and waking up to a warm and toasty room where the floors were never cold.

Olivia walked softly downstairs so as to not draw attention to herself. She peered into the kitchen and saw that Pastor Thomas and her mother were sitting at the kitchen table. They both had serious looks on their faces.

"How many were killed?" her mother asked.

"They are reporting at least 300 were killed and several more were injured."

Olivia gasped when she heard this. Her mother immediately turned in her direction. "Good morning, Olivia. Are you eavesdropping?"

"Well, kind of. I only heard that 300 people were killed. I did not hear the rest," Olivia said sheepishly. "What's going on?"

Her mother motioned to the empty chair. "You might as well sit down, and I will give you the rundown of what happened last night in Israel."

Her mother and Pastor Thomas went on to recap the events of last evening. According to news reports, Marcus Aldric agreed to allow Jews to gather on the Temple Mount around the unfinished temple on the first night of Hanukkah, which was last evening. Since the peace agreement last year, all religions were allowed to worship on the Temple Mount, as well as bring religious icons. They also opened up visiting hours to seven days a week from sunrise to sunset. They had estimated that there were more than 400,000 Jews as well as Christians gathered together to celebrate the beginning of Hanukkah as well as rejoice in the fact that they were able to worship on the Temple Mount freely. The security that was funded and controlled by the government of Jordan had become extremely lax. Apparently, a group of Iraqi Muslim radicals stormed the Temple Mount, entering through the four gates closest to the new temple. There were at least ten of them that had opened fire, killing hundreds of unarmed civilians, as well as injuring several others. It was mass chaos until the Israeli security forces were able to get control of the situation and kill the insurgents.

Olivia just sat and listened while her mom and Pastor Thomas described what happened last evening.

After finishing telling the news, Elizabeth got up and made a cup of coffee.

"Olivia, would you like one?"

Olivia nodded and added, "Extra cream, please."

Elizabeth poured the coffee, refreshed pastor Thomas's cup, and then sat back down.

"Apparently, several of the insurgents tried killing the two witnesses who were outside the Wailing Wall, but no matter what they did, the witnesses just kept standing and continued to preach."

Pastor Thomas interjected, "The two witnesses also threatened to stop the rains in Jerusalem for six months to serve as a reminder that Jesus is in control and that they are on this earth to represent Him."

"I'm sure that did not help the witnesses get on anybody's good side," Olivia said sarcastically.

"I'm sure you are right. It will only escalate the situation," Pastor Thomas stated.

"Well, what's going to happen next?" Olivia questioned.

"I'm going to talk about it this Saturday, but I think that this is the fifth seal. The fifth seal focuses on the suffering of Jesus's followers, which corresponds with Satan coming to terms with the fact that he is running out of time. God indicated in Revelation that He would protect some of His people, but some He would allow to be martyred," Pastor Thomas said with a grim expression.

"That means that we will shortly be moving into the sixth seal, right?" Olivia asked with a frown.

"I am afraid so, but that also means that we are closer to the rapture. Do not despair, Olivia: our time here on the earth is getting shorter."

"It is just so scary. The majority of what has been happening has not affected us significantly. We have been well prepared to ride out the famine. We have not seen the suffering that the other countries have seen, but I know that the next few months could get really difficult."

Elizabeth stood up, walked over to Olivia, and put an arm around her shoulders.

"You and Matt have been amazing through all of this. I have really seen you grow as people and in your walk with God. We will be fine. Just keep your eye on the prize…"

"I am so excited to see heaven. I just wish we did not have to go through this to get there."

Pastor Thomas nodded and said, "I agree, but I also think that we will appreciate it so much more when we do get there."

That Saturday night, Pastor Thomas called a special meeting to discuss the new events that transpired. The church members, like Olivia, were concerned about what would happen next. Pastor Thomas spent the entire hour discussing the sixth seal and how it could potentially impact them all.

"If we are to believe in Daniel's prophecy and Revelation, we should be through the first half of the tribulation around the beginning of July next year. That means we have from now until then to prepare for the sixth seal," Pastor Thomas informed the congregation.

Immediately hands went up requesting more information regarding the sixth seal and what Pastor Thomas anticipated would happen.

"Well, let's start from the beginning. John writes in Revelation that when the sixth seal is opened, there will be catastrophic events, which include a great earthquake. He also indicates that the sun will turn black, the moon will turn bloodred, and the stars will fall from the sky to the earth. With these catastrophic events, the mountains and islands will be moved from their current place." Pastor Thomas paused and looked around the room. "There have been many interpretations of these events, including theories that there will be a nuclear war, global earthquakes, or even volcanic eruptions. I have a theory myself, but again, I do not know for sure. Only God knows what He has planned for us."

After Pastor Thomas finished, Jake, an antique shop owner, asked, "How do we know that the rapture will take place during the middle of the tribulation? What if it does not? What do we do then?"

Several parishioners started nodding and murmuring to each other. Mark from Ingles Market chimed in, "We are all hoping that your theory regarding the midtribulation is correct, but what if you are wrong? Then we have to suffer through the last three and a half years, which will be horrible."

Pastor Thomas held up his hands.

"I know this is a very difficult time for everyone, and you have put a lot of faith into what I have been telling you. Just know that what I have been preaching to you these past two years has been either directly from the Bible or from God speaking to me. I would never intentionally mislead you."

Peter, a bookstore owner, spoke up, "We don't believe that you would intentionally tell us something that was not true, but what if you are wrong? You keep telling us to be prepared for the future, but I feel that we will not be if we are not raptured in July."

A voice from the back spoke up, "I don't believe now is the time to stop trusting Pastor Thomas."

Olivia turned to see who was speaking and was surprised that it was Austin, who had been unconvinced in the beginning.

"He has not misled us so far. Even before this all started, he warned us that it was coming. I know I was skeptical at first, but since seeing everything that has been going on, I don't know how any of you cannot believe in what Pastor Thomas has been saying."

Elizabeth stood up at that point and spoke, "I agree with Austin. Now is not the time to start questioning our faith. That is what the devil wants us to do. He is trying to divide us. Now is the time to stick together and do what we need to do to get through this. If the rapture does not happen, then so be it. We will face that when it comes. I happen to trust that Pastor Thomas will help us through whatever comes up next." At that, she sat back down.

Several of the parishioners clapped and nodded in agreement.

"Thank you, Elizabeth and Austin. I appreciate your support. It is natural for people to have doubts, and I want you to express them here. Do not think that there have been days I have doubted myself. When I do, I always go back to two things, the Word and prayer. If you are filled with uncertainty, reach for the Bible or pray to God that He will give you discernment. I don't have all the answers, but God does. Elizabeth is right. If the rapture does not occur, we will face that hurdle when it comes. For now, we need to get through these next few months and pray that the end is near."

Pastor Thomas spent the next ten minutes answering questions, but the atmosphere had changed from challenging to more looking for reassurance.

When the meeting was over, Caleb and Olivia went to the back of the church to have some time alone. They had not had much time together since Thanksgiving, so they made plans to spend the day together after church tomorrow.

Olivia left the meeting with mixed feelings. She was worried about the future but also excited to spend time with Caleb. She felt apprehensive about the other members' concerns and was afraid their doubts would spread to others. She agreed with her mother that now was not the time to start questioning Pastor Thomas. Olivia made a resolution that she would continue to do whatever she needed to do to support Pastor Thomas and alleviate any doubts the others had.

Olivia and Caleb planned another Christmas party at the church for the Friday before Christmas. Olivia was excited about the party but also had a feeling of sadness, as she knew it would be her last Christmas on the earth. She knew it was foolish, as nothing could be better than heaven, but the other part of her was sad to let go of the past and her life as it was currently.

Clara invited her to go with her to get her hair done prior to the party. Clara's mother was good friends with one of the hairdressers downtown and offered to do the girls' hair at a discounted rate. Olivia was a little hesitant, as she always did her hair and did not want anyone messing with it, but she conceded, and they drove downtown Friday afternoon.

While waiting, Olivia thumbed through the books the hairdresser kept in the salon with all the newest hairstyles. She had not had her hair cut, other than trims, since she was a little girl. Her long hair had always been her one pride. As she sat there, Olivia thought about how much time and energy she spent on her hair. She was always worried about how it looked. The more she thought about it, the more she realized that it was not Christian to be obsessed with her looks. At that moment, she decided that she would eliminate the areas in her life that kept her from focusing on the Lord completely.

Clara was shocked when she saw the end result. Olivia had twenty-four inches of her hair cut off. It was styled into a shoulder-length layered bob. The hairdresser had left her blond hair natural wavy, which framed her face and made her look more mature.

"I love it, Olivia!" Clara exclaimed. "I cannot believe you did it, though. As long as I have known you, you have had long hair. It looks great on you!"

"Thanks. I really just wanted to actually stop focusing on my hair and anything else that is taking my attention of what our real mission is, which is spreading the word about Jesus."

Tina, the hairdresser, interjected with a laugh, "Well, she spent the past forty-five minutes preaching to me. I'm ready to join your church."

"We would love to have you. I know that you were kept captive by me, as you couldn't go anywhere, but really just try the church out. You have nothing to lose and everything to gain."

Clara nodded in agreement. "We really would."

Tina shrugged her shoulders and gave a noncommittal maybe.

Olivia turned to Clara.

"Oh my gosh, your hair looks great!"

Margaret, the stylist, had given Clara a braided natural updo that accentuated her high cheekbones and long neck.

"Why, thank you. I do love how it turned out." Clara grinned as she spun around to show off the full effect of her new hairdo.

The girls both paid with their Terra-Cash account and tipped their stylist well before driving back to Olivia's house. It did not take them long to get ready for the party. Clara helped Olivia with her makeup, and they had their dresses laid out, ready to go. Both girls chose to wear black tonight. Olivia chose a long-sleeved form-fitting high-collared dress that fit her long, lean body perfectly. It landed just below her knees. She added a gold cross necklace with a long chain to break up the severe black. The only other jewelry she wore was the charm bracelet her mom had given her for her birthday the previous year.

Clara's dress was a knee-length, three-quarter sleeve, with a peekaboo jeweled waist. The girls both admired each other as they looked in the mirror before heading downstairs to say goodbye to Olivia's mom.

Matt actually agreed to go to the party and was already downstairs, waiting. He had dressed in a pair of black pants, with a black dress shirt and red tie.

Olivia and Clara both remarked on how handsome he looked. Matt blushed and looked away, but not before Olivia noted that he looked secretly pleased.

"You two don't look so bad either. Took you long enough to get ready, though," he said with a grimace.

Clara punched him in the arm.

"You guys have it so easy. Shower, brush your hair, and get dressed. That's it. We have to do our hair, our makeup, our nails, and then get dressed. It is a long process."

Olivia punched his other arm playfully.

"Yeah, what she said. Now, is everyone ready to go?" She yelled into the kitchen, "Mom, we are leaving!"

"All right, all right. I'm coming. I need to take some pictures. Wait right there!" Elizabeth rushed into the living room. "Oh my heavens, you girls look beautiful! Olivia, your haircut is fabulous with that dress."

"What about me? How do I look?" Matt questioned.

"Very handsome. You look like a younger version of your dad. He would have been so proud of both of you," Elizabeth said, tearing up. She quickly shook it off and began snapping pictures of the three of them.

"Now, let me get a few with just Olivia and Matt." They knew not to argue as their mom was very persistent when it came to taking pictures before any event. She had been that way for as long as Olivia could remember. When they were done with the two of them, Elizabeth got a few of just Olivia and Clara.

"Mrs. Ahren, can you text me those pictures?"

"Sure, Clara. Have a good time tonight. Do not stay out too late. Matt, keep an eye on them," she said jokingly.

Olivia gave her mom a quick hug before heading out the door. The night was very cool, in the low thirties, so they all put on their coats before walking out into the brisk night air. Olivia got into her Volkswagen with Clara sitting in the passenger seat and Matt in the back.

They chatted all the way to the church and arrived just as the party was beginning. Pastor Thomas and a few of the other parents had made all the arrangements for the party. Olivia was happy that she did not have to be part of the planning.

Caleb was waiting for her outside and walked in with them. When Olivia took off her coat, Caleb gave a low wolf whistle.

"Wow, you look great. You mentioned you got your hair cut when I talked to you earlier, but you did not say how much you had gotten cut off."

Olivia smiled and did a ballerina turn in the church lobby. "Well, do you like it?"

"It looks great. I loved your hair before, but this really fits you," Caleb said as he eyed her appreciatively.

He turned to Clara. "You look great too, Clara. Those dresses are both beautiful," Caleb said with sincerity. He took all of their coats and laid them on a table specifically for that purpose.

Caleb grabbed Olivia's hand, and they made their way to the church basement where the party was being held. The room was starting to fill up with young adults and kids from the church.

Emma and Seth had arrived early, as their father was helping out Pastor Thomas with the setup. Marty arrived a few minutes later, and their group was complete. Matt hung out with them for a while until his friend Mark showed up, and the two of them went to hang out with their group of friends.

Olivia made a special point to spend time with Marty, who she had not seen in a while. She was pleasantly surprised to find that she was handling her mother's death well. Marty explained to her that with everything going on in the world, she knew it would not be long before she saw her mother again. "It really is a choice, Olivia. You can choose to be miserable, or you can choose happiness, and I chose happiness."

"You are so right, Marty. I'm glad you chose to be happy. We have missed hanging out with you," Olivia said and then reached over and pulled Marty into a hug. The girls soon joined the rest of the group.

The night went by fast. Olivia stayed until after midnight and closed the party out. Olivia, Clara, and Caleb all offered to help clean up, but Pastor Thomas shooed them home. He reassured them he had it all under control.

Olivia, Clara, and Matt drove home in silence, listening to Christmas music on the Christian radio station. They all seemed lost in their thoughts. Olivia was reliving the last slow dance she had with Caleb. He held her close with his arms encircling her waist, and they swayed to the music in perfect harmony. She just hoped that they would get another chance to dance.

## Chapter Twenty-One

I watched as he opened the sixth seal. There was a great earthquake. The sun turned black like sackcloth made of goat hair, the whole moon turned blood red, and the stars in the sky fell to earth, as figs drop from a fig tree when shaken by a strong wind. The heavens receded like a scroll being rolled up, and every mountain and island was removed from its place. Then the kings of the earth, the princes, the generals, the rich, the mighty, and everyone else, both slave and free, hid in caves and among the rocks of the mountains. They called to the mountains and the rocks, "Fall on us and hide us from the face of him who sits on the throne and from the wrath of the Lamb! For the great day of their wrath has come, and who can withstand it?"

*Revelation 6:12-17*

### Friday, March 30, 2029

#### Passover

The temple was completed on the last day in February, and the Jewish community had made preparations to enter the sanctuary and begin sacrifices on Passover.

Since Passover was tonight, Olivia decided to do some research on the holiday. She really did not know a lot about Jewish traditions, and she wanted to see what it entailed. According to the article she found, Passover commemorates the Jews' liberation from slavery. She read that the holiday is often celebrated for eight days, and on those days, only unleavened bread, called matzo, may be eaten. The article explained that matzo symbolizes both the Hebrews' suffering while in bondage and the haste with which they left Egypt in the course of the Exodus.

According to her Google search, the main feature of the ancient Passover ceremony was the sacrificial rite of the paschal lamb and its consumption on the eve of Passover. Olivia thought this was barbaric. All she could do was picture the sweet innocent lamb being slaughtered. She was glad to read that these sacrifices eventually stopped when the Temple was destroyed in AD 70. Olivia knew from the Old Testament that there were several references to sacrifices being done to atone for the Jews' sins; she just could not imagine it being done in this day and age. The Jewish religion still celebrated Passover, but until this year, they had done it without the animal sacrifices. Olivia was happy that the Christian religion felt the need for animal sacrifices no longer existed, as the sacrifice of Christ paid the debt of sin for all humanity, both Jew and Gentile. She had several friends in Sarasota that were Jewish, and she knew that they did not believe that Jesus was the Son of Man and therefore did not believe that he atoned for their sins. *Wow,* she thought, *This is a big deal for the Jewish community.*

For the past couple of months, Pastor Thomas had prepared the church for the potential upcoming events, which included the Jews resuming sacrifices in the temple. True to the witnesses' word, there had been no rain in Israel since Hanukkah. The Jewish community felt that it was God's way of punishing them, and they felt that by resuming the sacrifices, they would be back in God's favor.

Olivia was worried about what the next couple of months would bring. Up until now, everything Pastor Thomas had warned the church about had pretty much come to light. It was only a few months away from the date he predicted the rapture would take place. Olivia and her friends had been working diligently, trying to reach as many people as possible to help them accept Jesus as their Lord and Savior before it would be too late.

Olivia and Kylie had been talking regularly since Christmas. Sara and Mike had been instrumental in getting Kylie involved in the church in their new town. The best thing that could have happened to her was getting away from Sarasota and the influence of their friends there. Kylie was actually working with the outreach team to minister to others, and Olivia could definitely tell the difference in her attitude. Kylie was much less focused on herself and seemed to actually care about what others thought and felt. Olivia was so happy for her friend. Kylie never visited Olivia in Blue Ridge, but she knew that she would see her again.

Emma, Seth, Clara, and Caleb all had been kept busy working with Pastor Thomas. Matt and his friend Mark also had joined the group when they were not doing schoolwork. Olivia thought it was kind of ridiculous for Matt to continue in school, but Elizabeth thought it was important to continue with a routine, and she also felt it kept him out of trouble.

Olivia was impressed by how much Matt had matured over the past couple of years. He had turned sixteen in February and, like Olivia, had gotten a car for his birthday. Elizabeth continued to try to normalize everything in their life, and Olivia appreciated it. They had gone out to dinner at Olivia's favorite restaurant, where she had spent her birthday three years previously. It was surprising how much could change in a few years. While eating dinner on her sixteenth birthday, Olivia had been blissfully unaware of what the next few years would bring. As difficult as times had been, she wouldn't have changed a thing. Olivia was happy with the person she had become and knew that if she and her mother had not gone to that meeting with Pastor Thomas, her life might have gone down a totally different path.

Caleb and Olivia generally went out on Friday nights, spending their time walking hand in hand downtown or having a picnic while sitting in the park. Their friends would occasionally join them, but usually, it was just the two of them. Tonight they decided to stay in, so Caleb brought food to Olivia's house.

After dinner, Matt and their mother joined them in the living room, and they played a game of scrabble. They had the TV on in the background, listening to the evening news. When the reporter turned their focus to the resumption of sacrifices in the temple, Elizabeth turned up the TV volume to hear what was being said. According to the newscaster, the Passover sacrifice took place at 2:00 p.m., which was 7:00 a.m. eastern standard time, and apparently, it had gone well, with no violence or issues with the Muslims.

"Today was a historical moment for the Jewish community. It had been almost 2,000 years since the last Passover sacrifice had been made in the Jewish temple. Jewish leaders are rejoicing today as they feel that the Third Temple has given the Jews a central location once again to worship and fully keep God's covenant with them."

The newscaster went to live footage from the Temple Mount where they had interviewed Benjamin Click, a leader of the Temple Movement, earlier in the day.

Blake Lancaster, the special correspondent with ABC News, was speaking from the Temple Mount: "I am here today with Rabbi Benjamin Glick, who is director of the Temple Mount Faithful Movement. Can you tell me how you are feeling today?"

"Well, Blake, our organization has been making preparations since 1987 for the rebuilding of the Third Temple. In terms of our mission, we felt we could not reach our spiritual status without the temple. For years, we have been training priests for this day. We feel confident that the problems faced by the Jewish people today will be solved now that the temple is rebuilt and we have reestablished the sacrifices. In fact, 202 out of the 613 commandments in the Torah cannot be performed without a temple. Our organization, as well as the majority of the Jewish community, feel that this Third Temple will bring the light back into the world that left when the Lord's divine presence departed after the temple was destroyed in AD 70."

"It appears that the Jewish community has come together and supported this third temple, but what about the other religions? Have you had a negative response?" Blake questioned.

"At first, we were very concerned, especially after the massacre on Hanukkah at the site of the temple…but since that time, Prophet D'Angelo and President Aldric have been in full support of the building of the temple, which has helped our cause immensely. Of course, not everyone has been for it, but since its completion, we have had nothing but a positive response. Once they saw that we were transforming the Temple Mount to its original sacred role as a place of worship, which is to be shared by Jews, Muslims, and Christians, they stopped the protests."

Blake smiled into the camera.

"Thank you, Rabbi Glick. It was a pleasure to talk to you today. Later in the broadcast, Prophet D'Angelo and President Marcus Aldric will be speaking from the Temple Mount, so please stay tuned for their message of unity on this momentous day."

Elizabeth was the first to speak, "Well, I guess it is only a matter of time before the next seal is broken."

Caleb nodded his head somberly.

"I'm afraid you are correct. I better get going. Dad has probably been watching the news all day and will want someone to decompress with."

"Okay, I'll walk you out to the car," Olivia said with a smile.

After they all said their goodbyes, Caleb grabbed his coat from the kitchen, and the two of them walked out into the cold night. When they got to his car, he pulled Olivia close to him in a tight hug. Olivia was reluctant to break away, as she felt so safe and secure in his arms. Caleb pulled back first and gave her a soft kiss on the lips before opening his car door.

"I'll see you tomorrow?" he questioned.

"Of course, I would not miss this meeting for anything. I'm glad your father has moved the meetings to weekly again. I think it helps keep us all focused and also gives us a sense of togetherness."

"I agree. That is exactly why he did it. He was getting so many calls and questions throughout the month that it is easier just to meet weekly to go over everyone's questions and also put everyone at ease."

Olivia nodded, saying, "I agree. With everything going on, it is a bit overwhelming and scary."

Caleb gave her another kiss on the lips and then got into his car.

"Drive carefully. I'll see you tomorrow," Olivia called out and waved as she watched his car drive away.

Olivia walked back into the warm house and sat next to her mom on the couch. Elizabeth had turned the TV off and had put a Christian music station on through Alexa. Matt had gone upstairs to play his video games. Elizabeth put her arm around Olivia and pulled her close. They sat there for a while, not saying anything, just enjoying the time together.

Finally, Olivia broke the silence, "Mom, I'm scared."

Elizabeth tightened her hold and said sadly, "Me too. These last three years have been crazy with their ups and downs. I have loved spending all this time with you and Matt and working alongside you both in spreading the word of Jesus, but it has also been such a sad time for our friends and families that have lost so much."

"I know. I think of Kylie and how she lost both parents. Marty and Caleb lost their mother. Emma and Seth basically lost their mother. I know she is still alive, but they are afraid that she won't go to heaven because she does not believe in Jesus. She's into all that nature-and-higher-power stuff," Olivia said sadly. She turned to her mother with tears in her eyes. "I can't imagine living an eternity without you there with me."

"Well, it is a good thing you will not have to. I am looking forward to the time we are all together again. I can't wait for your father to see what two amazing adults you and Matt have grown into."

Olivia smiled and hugged her mom.

"I can't wait to see Katie. She won't believe I finally cut my hair," she said jokingly.

"I love you, Olivia. I'm going upstairs to get some sleep. You should too."

"I'll be up in a minute. I just want to sit here for a little while."

They said their goodnights. Olivia sat on the couch and listened to the Christian radio station until she could hardly keep her eyes open and finally gave in and went to bed.

## Chapter Twenty-Two

### June 25, 2029

"Hurry up, let's get everything set up before we miss the eclipse," Clara said excitedly.

They were all gathered at Olivia's house in preparation for watching the total lunar eclipse. It was 10:20 p.m., and the eclipse was scheduled to begin at 10:30 p.m. Elizabeth had made snacks for the event, and Olivia had laid out four large blankets in the backyard for them to have an optimal view of the event. Caleb and his dad, Marty, Seth, Emma, as well as Matt's friend Mark were all there to watch the cosmic event.

"All right, Clara, relax. Everything is ready," Olivia said as she carried out a tray of food to set in the middle of the group of blankets. Elizabeth was right behind her with another tray of food, and Matt had a cooler filled with drinks.

Caleb had a radio set up on a table nearby with the Christian radio station playing.

"All right, everyone, grab a seat on a blanket," Elizabeth stated as she motioned toward the ground.

As soon as everyone was seated, Elizabeth handed out drinks, gave everyone a paper plate, and told them to help themselves to some food. She and Olivia had spent the afternoon making a variety of snacks for the event, which included chicken wings, ham and cheese sliders, pizza rolls, spinach dip bites, cheese and crackers, as well as vegetables and dip.

They all loaded up their plates and sat back down, awaiting the eclipse. Olivia, Clara, Caleb sat together on one blanket. It was a warm summer evening with a slightly cooler breeze.

Clara had come up with the idea for them to all get together to watch the eclipse. When Elizabeth heard the idea, she decided to make it into a small party. It had been a while since the group had gotten together just for fun. They had been spending the majority of their time these last few months proselytizing to anyone that would listen to them. Pastor Thomas had been very insistent that they reach as many people as possible in these last days.

Right at 10:30 p.m., the eclipse began. Olivia could not remember a time when she actually had seen a lunar eclipse, and she did not realize that it would be very anticlimactic.

"I guess I was expecting something more exciting," Olivia said with a little laugh.

"Have you never seen an eclipse before? It takes a while. According to the news, it will not be at maximum eclipse until around 11:22 p.m.," Seth said with authority.

"Well, in that case, I guess I won't spend the next hour just staring at the moon," Clara said jokingly.

They all joined in laughing and then began talking among themselves. They spent the next hour listening to music, eating, drinking, and enjoying each other's company. Seth had set the alarm on his Apple Watch, and right at 11:22 p.m., it went off, and he reminded them to look up. The moon was completely covered in the shadow of the earth, and it appeared red in the night sky.

Just as they were all oohing and awing over the display, they felt the ground begin to shake. The food on the ground was bouncing all over, and the radio fell off the table. It lasted for what seemed like an eternity but, in truth, was only a few seconds. Olivia had grabbed onto Caleb as everyone was trying to keep their food and drinks from falling over. Once the earth settled, Pastor Thomas went over to the radio to set it back on the table. There was dead silence for a few minutes and when the host of the radio station, Christina, came back on.

Christina's voice was shaky when she stated that she had felt what she thought was an earthquake in the studio. Her station manager broke in and informed Christina that reports were coming in from all over the world with news of earthquakes and volcanic activity. Christina asked everyone to stop and pray for the safety of all her listeners and anyone affected by the natural catastrophe.

Everyone just stood around looking at each other, and then Christina played "Run to the Father" by Cody Carnes. When the music started playing, Clara immediately joined in. Soon they were all singing loudly and passionately with the warm breeze flowing around them. At that moment, Olivia knew everything was going to be all right. She felt the Holy Spirit present with her and her friends. Tears were running down her face as she sang the words, "I run to the Father, I fall into grace; I'm done with the hiding. No reason to wait."[9]

As she looked around, she saw that she was not the only one affected and was overwhelmed with her love for her friends and her family.

When the song ended, Pastor Thomas had them all gather together and hold hands as he prayed.

"Dear Lord, heavenly Father, You know that we are in the midst of many great dangers. Grant us strength and protection to support us in all perils and carry us through all temptations; help us guide our minds from harmful instruction, and grant us discernment to recognize truth. Help us to not fear or be in dread of what is about to be, for it is the Lord our God who goes with us. He will not leave us or forsake us. We know that the only safe place is in Jesus and that this home on the earth is only temporary. Amen."

Caleb started reciting the Lord's Prayer, and they all joined in. Once they had finished the prayer, they wandered into Olivia's house.

Elizabeth turned on the news to see what was happening around the world. The local station had reports that several of the volcanos in the Ring of Fire, which is a horseshoe-shaped area that stretches around the edge of the Pacific Ocean, all erupted at once, as well as others in Europe and the Middle East. News reports were coming in from all over the world that there was considerable destruction as the eruption of the volcanos caused massive earthquakes. Several countries were bracing for tsunamis. Ash was launched into the air, and scientists expected that it would cover the world in the next few days, completely blocking sunlight. And, as if things couldn't get any worse, the toxic volcanic gases would create acid rain. The rain would make the oceans even more acidic, killing off coral reefs. Marine life would suffer an extinction event.

"This is it, isn't it, Pastor Thomas? This is the sixth seal?" Clara asked grimly.

"I'm afraid so. In the next few months, there will be total devastation to the planet as a consequence of the natural disasters that took place tonight. We are prepared. We have enough water and food to get us through until the rapture."

Emma looked doubtful and asked, "But what if the rapture doesn't happen? What are we going to do?"

Olivia walked up to Emma and gave her a hug.

"It is going to be okay. Continue to keep the faith. We will be fine no matter what happens."

Emma stepped back from Olivia and wiped the tears from her face. "You are right. I'm sorry. Just sometimes, this is so overwhelming. And I really worry about my mom."

Pastor Thomas nodded sadly. "I know, Emma, we all have someone we are worried about. You have all done an amazing job of reaching out to our neighbors, friends, and family. We have one more chance to reach as many people as possible this Sunday."

"Why? What's happening on Sunday?" Clara questioned.

"We are going to have a group baptism in Lake Blue Ridge at Morganton Point Recreation Area."

"Where is that?" Elizabeth asked.

"It's about seven miles from downtown Georgia. I have flyers made up, and we will start distributing them tomorrow. I plan to put them all over Blue Ridge, Ellijay, Blairsville, and all the neighboring towns. I also convinced Victory 91.5, the local Christian radio station, to let me put an announcement on there. They will be running it the next few days."

"Wow, when did you put this all in place?" Caleb questioned.

"I have been working on it for a while, but it all came together last night. I knew that it was crucial that we did it this Sunday."

"What can we do to help?" Elizabeth offered.

"I will need you all to take a town tomorrow and start putting up flyers, and on Sunday, I will need all of you to help me do the baptisms. I'm not sure how many people will respond, but I think we will need all hands on deck."

Everyone nodded in agreement, and they spent the next half an hour coming up with a plan for distributing the flyers. It was almost 1:00 a.m. by the time they finished formulating their strategy. Elizabeth offered to have them all spend the night, but Pastor Thomas and Caleb decided to go home. Marty's father also insisted she come home. Since her mother's death, her father had been much more protective. After checking in with their parents, the rest of the group decided to have a camp out in the living room.

Even though it was late and past Olivia's usual bedtime, she had a difficult time falling asleep. She knew that she should not worry and should put her faith in Jesus, but there was still a part of her that was fearful of what the future would bring.

The next morning Olivia awoke to the smell of bacon. She looked outside, and it still appeared dark outside. She looked at her smartwatch and noticed it was already 9:00 a.m. It appeared that everyone else was still sleeping. She quietly got up and ran upstairs to brush her teeth and change her clothes. By the time she got back downstairs, everyone else was awake and in the kitchen helping Elizabeth get breakfast ready.

"Oh, there you are. I thought you might still be sleeping," Elizabeth remarked when she saw Olivia walk into the kitchen.

"I actually was the first one up, but I wanted to change my clothes. Good morning, everyone. Mom, any update on the news?"

"There has been quite a bit. The majority of the earthquakes had hit in the Middle East, as well as the countries located on the Pacific Ocean. California has been almost completely obliterated as well as Oregon and Washington. They are anticipating thousands of deaths. They have not even been able to get into the wreckage yet due to the instability of the area. Large craters have opened up, and power lines are down. It's quite the mess."

"What about here, in Georgia and Florida?" Olivia asked worriedly.

"Well, it looks like we pretty much went unscathed. There is a little damage, but nothing major. Florida has had damage to the coastline due to massive waves." Elizabeth stopped what she was doing and looked around with a troubled look on her face. "The West Coast, Korea, Japan, as well as the Middle East were hit especially hard due to the volcanos and earthquakes. There have been horrible tsunamis that have formed and taken out most of the Philippines, Indonesia, Malaysia, Thailand, and Vietnam. It is just horrible."

Clara was busy making eggs when she turned and asked, "How long do they anticipate that it will remain dark outside?"

Seth piped in, "They said it might be months before we will see the sun again, and it will most likely change the global climate for decades. The farther away from the eruptions, the better, but there will definitely be food shortages and global cooling. When Mount Tambora erupted in Indonesia back in the 1800s, it killed tens of thousands of people, and they said it caused the temperature on the earth to drop by as much as three degrees."

Matt and Mark were at the counter playing on the Nintendo Switches when Matt looked up, saying, "Wow, that is crazy. I'm glad we won't be around for all of that."

Elizabeth nodded in agreement. "Me too. Matt, can you set the table? Olivia, please get the orange juice and milk out, as well as glasses. Breakfast is almost ready, everyone."

The next few days, Pastor Thomas and the team were busy passing out flyers, going from business to business to tell anyone they saw about Jesus, and inviting them to come on Sunday for baptism. Pastor Thomas was on a mission to reach as many people as possible before Sunday. Olivia and Caleb teamed up and drove to Blairsville to spread the word.

Olivia could not get over how bizarre it was to be out in the day and have it appear almost like night. The sun was almost completely obliterated by the ash that continued to spew into the stratosphere from a couple of the volcanos that were still active. The ash itself had not reached Blue Ridge, but it definitely had affected the temperature already. It was the end of June, and the temperature was only in the high fifties. Olivia wondered how Sarasota was fairing.

She had spoken to Kylie the day after it happened, and thankfully, her guardians were well prepared for the upcoming events. Olivia was very thankful that Mike and Sara had moved Kylie and that they were true followers of Jesus.

Olivia enjoyed the time she had with Caleb. The drive was about half an hour, and they spent almost five hours walking around Blairsville, putting up flyers. The response was mixed. There definitely was a feeling of desperation in the air. Olivia felt that, compared to a year ago, many of the people they met were more open to hearing what they had to say, especially since many of the news outlets were reporting that it was the end of the world.

Once they were finished, she and Caleb walked the town square, found a diner right in the center, and grabbed lunch. Olivia got a grilled chicken sandwich and fries, and Caleb got a Pepper Jack cheeseburger with onion rings. They were both starving and ate their lunch quietly, reflecting on the day.

On the drive home, they were both quiet, enjoying the peaceful ride and listening to a Christian radio station. The news reports between songs were pretty grim. It was difficult for Olivia to wrap her head around all the destruction that was taking place throughout the world.

President Aldric and Allesandro D'Angelo were planning to travel to the Middle East later in the week to address the devastation caused by the volcano in Saudi Arabia. Air travel had been completely stopped due to the ash in the atmosphere and poor visibility. Olivia was not sure how they would get to the Middle East, but considering one was the Antichrist and the other was the false prophet, she figured that they would manage it somehow.

# Chapter Twenty-Three

When he opened the seventh seal, there was silence in heaven for about half an hour. And I saw the seven angels who stand before God, and seven trumpets were given to them. Another angel, who had a golden censer, came and stood at the altar. He was given much incense to offer, with the prayers of all God's people, on the golden altar in front of the throne. The smoke of the incense, together with the prayers of God's people, went up before God from the angel's hand. Then the angel took the censer, filled it with fire from the altar, and hurled it on the earth; and there came peals of thunder, rumblings, flashes of lightning and an earthquake.

*Revelation 8:1-5*

## Sunday, July 1, 2029

Matt and Olivia were ready to go to church early as they knew it was going to be a momentous day. Caleb had informed Olivia that at least a hundred people had signed up for baptism this afternoon at Lake Blue Ridge.

Pastor Thomas had arranged for several members of the church to assist with the baptism, including Olivia and her friends. Matt had declined to help with the actual baptism but would be there to help with the crowd control. Olivia would be working with her mother to baptize people. She had never done anything like this and felt a mixture of excitement as well as anxiety. Olivia knew how important this was and did not want to mess anything up. Elizabeth spent the morning reassuring her that if she prayed to God and followed her heart, it would all work out.

The morning church service was overflowing with people. There were not enough seats in the sanctuary, so many were standing against the walls. Olivia had never seen the church so full; she did not recognize many of the people. She felt this was a good sign, as that meant their last-ditch effort to prophesize to people had actually worked.

Following the 11:00 a.m. church service, the group drove to Morganton Point Recreation Area. Normally, the day would have been bright and sunny and the water temperature would be in the low seventies this time of year, but today, the temperature was a very cool sixty-three degrees. Olivia was not looking forward to going into the cold water. In Sarasota, she would not even go into her pool unless the temperature of the water was above eighty-six degrees.

The baptism was set for 1:00 p.m. The recreation area usually charged cars to park, but Pastor Thomas was able to get a special use permit, and the Forest Service waived the usual fees. The church members had gotten there early to set up and devise a plan as to how to manage the crowd. Once they determined the best course of action, Pastor Thomas and the crew waited until people arrived.

Shortly before 1:00 p.m., cars started pulling up. Olivia was excited to see that their hard work had paid off. Soon the parking lot was full, and people were parking on the grass.

Matt and several of the younger members of the church were directing people where to go. As soon as it appeared that everyone had arrived, Pastor Thomas got on the back of his pickup where

Jeff, the DJ, had set up a sound system and microphone so he could speak to the entire crowd. Olivia looked around, and she estimated that there were at least 200 people there. She noticed several people that she and Caleb had spoken to while handing out flyers in Blairsville, as well as locals, including Tina, her hairdresser.

Pastor Thomas welcomed everyone and prayed over the baptism. Once he finished, he directed the crowd to line up in an orderly fashion, and the four groups of two, including Olivia and Elizabeth, went into the frigid water. Marty's father's role was to help coordinate the flow of the individuals who were there to be baptized.

Olivia could not believe how cold the water was. She had on leggings and a long sleeve shirt, but she was still freezing. Their first participant entered the water and joined Elizabeth and Olivia.

Elizabeth set a comforting hand on the young girl's shoulder.

"Hi, my name is Elizabeth, and this is my daughter, Olivia."

The girl, who looked to be about Olivia's age, responded shyly, "Hi, I'm McKayla."

"I'm so glad you came out today. What prompted you to be baptized?" Elizabeth questioned.

"Well, my mom and dad saw the fliers in the Walmart in Ellijay and started talking about it. I have been really scared about what is going on, and then, when I saw the flier, I got an overwhelming feeling of peace. I am not sure what happened, but I knew I had to come out here today."

Olivia's eyes welled up with tears.

"Oh my gosh, McKayla, you were filled with the Holy Spirit. I am so happy for you."

McKayla smiled back, and Elizabeth and Olivia prayed over her. Once she declared that she had accepted Jesus as her Lord and

Savior, they immersed her completely in the water. When she came up, McKayla was laughing and gave them both a heartfelt hug.

"Thank you so much! I'm so glad we came out today. I already feel a weight lifted off of me," Mckayla said happily.

The rest of the afternoon went very similarly. They were in the freezing water for over an hour, and after the first few minutes, Olivia had not even noticed. Once they had baptized the last person, they walked out of the water to Marty's dad, who was holding a warm blanket out to them.

"I thought I would be freezing, but I was so energized by the work we did here today that I did not even feel it after the initial shock," Olivia remarked.

"I know. I was worried about you. You never liked cold water, but you were really a trooper today. I cannot tell you how proud I am of you. I wish your father were here to see this," Elizabeth said as she pulled Olivia in for a hug.

"Thanks, Mom. I wish he were here too. I really enjoyed today. I am so glad we did this! I think we reached a lot of people."

Olivia was starting to feel the cold now that she was just standing around. She grabbed her mom's keys and went to the car to turn on the heat. Soon Clara had joined her in the front seat.

"Oh my gosh, it is cold out there when you are dripping wet," Clara said through chattering teeth.

"I'll put your seat warmer on; you will be toasty in no time."

"Thanks. That was amazing. I don't think I have ever experienced anything like that. How about you?" Clara asked.

"Me neither. I definitely felt the Holy Spirit working in me today. I was somewhat scared to baptize people. I did not think I was the right person for the job, but as soon as the first girl came up to us, I knew I could do it," Olivia said proudly.

Clara started laughing.

"Remember when we first met and Pastor Thomas wanted us to go out and preach to others? We all were hesitant to do it. We did not feel that we were qualified. Now, look at us! We are baptizing people and bringing them to Jesus."

Olivia chuckled at the thought of how insecure they were in spreading the word of Jesus. "You are so right. We have definitely changed in the last three years, and definitely for the better."

"You are so right. I'm glad you moved to Blue Ridge. I know that it was not under the best circumstances, but I believe God brought you here for a reason. Think about how many people you have brought to Christ in the past couple of years."

"Thanks. I would never have thought that the move here would have been my saving grace," Olivia said sincerely.

That evening Olivia and her mom were sitting in the living room watching the 11:00 p.m. nightly news when a special report from Jerusalem came on. According to the newscaster, President Aldric and Prophet D'Angelo had met with the World Council of Religious Leaders and decided to stop the animal sacrifices in the temple. The world council felt that the recent events were in direct relation to not only the sacrifices but also the two protestors outside the Wailing Wall. President Aldric ordered the Israeli security forces to execute the two men. According to the reports, they were put to death at 2:00 a.m. Israeli time. President Aldric ordered their bodies to be on display at the Wailing Wall to bear witness to his commitment to ensuring that the world is safe from all forces of evil. The camera panned to a large group of Israelis outside the Wailing Wall, celebrating the death of these two men. The newscaster reported that many felt that recent events were directly related to these two men and celebrated their death.

Elizabeth shook her head in sadness.

"Well, it appears that all of John's premonitions from Revelation are coming true."

"Does this mean that we only have a matter of days if Pastor Thomas is correct about the rapture?" Olivia questioned.

"That is correct. I have an idea. How about we invite all of your friends and their parents over on Tuesday to celebrate?"

"I'm not sure everyone will think it is a celebration, but I like the idea, Mom. I would like to spend as much time as possible with my friends and you guys as possible. We don't know what will happen in the future."

"Great, sounds like a plan. Tomorrow, we will make all the arrangements. I have enough food and drinks. We will throw a going-away party for all of us," Elizabeth said with a chuckle.

Tuesday, July 3, 2021

Elizabeth, Olivia, and Matt were able to pull everything together by Tuesday evening. Fortunately, everyone was on board with the going-away party, and all offered to bring their favorite dish.

Olivia decided to dress up and wore the outfit she wore for the first Christmas party they had in Blue Ridge. The other girls followed suit and wore their favorite dresses. The men did not feel the need to get dressed up and wore more casual clothes.

Clara was the first to arrive with her mom. She looked lovely in a simple sleeveless black sheath dress. Caleb and Pastor Thomas arrived next and brought homemade chili, which according to Caleb, was the best chili in the world. Seth, Emma, and their father came with fried chicken fingers, and Marty and her dad brought guacamole. By the time everyone arrived, the food table was overflowing. Olivia's mouth was watering when she just looked at all the food. Matt had set up coolers of soda, water, and ice teas in the living room.

The atmosphere at first was subdued and somewhat tense. Olivia sensed that everyone was on edge, and she made a concerted effort to put everyone at ease.

"Pastor Thomas, can you say a prayer before we dig into all this wonderful food?"

"I would love to, Olivia." He then proceeded to say a blessing over the food as well as all of the people present. "I also want you to know that no matter what happens in the next few days, I am extremely proud of each and every one of you. I have seen you all grow in your faith and commitment to the Lord. On Sunday, I was amazed at you, young folks, and the effect you have had on this community. We don't even know how many people we have brought to Jesus. Give yourselves all a hand. I love you all."

The group all joined in with Pastor Thomas, clapping for themselves and each other. The rest of the night was filled with joy and happiness. They had their fill of food, played music, danced, and reminisced over the events of the past few years.

Olivia went to bed that night with a peace she had not felt in a long time. She knew that whatever tomorrow brought, she was safe and secure in Jesus's love and did not have to worry about her future. She fell asleep with a smile on her face and thoughts of heaven in her head.

# Epilogue

> But after the three and a half days the breath of life from God entered them, and they stood on their feet, and terror struck those who saw them. Then they heard a loud voice from heaven saying to them, "Come up here." And they went up to heaven in a cloud, while their enemies looked on them.
>
> *Revelation 11:11-12*

The next morning, alerts were going off on phones throughout the world. People were missing everywhere. Newscasters were reporting that people had mysteriously disappeared in the night.

Special reports were being broadcast on every TV and radio station across the world. Social media was going crazy. Not only were people missing, but the two murdered witnesses who were so disrespectfully displayed on the streets of Jerusalem had been recorded by cell phones miraculously arising. Bystanders reported that a bright light surrounded them, and all video had cut off at that point. The crowd that had surrounded the witnesses swore that they had stood up and then ascended into the heavens. There were reports that those that had witnessed this incredible event were suddenly blinded after looking into the bright light.

Although the world was in chaos, several homes in Blue Ridge were quiet. The small town was silent except for a few who were left behind.

# Notes

1. Revelation 6:2 (KJV).
2. Revelation 13:7 (NIV).
3. Candice Lucey, "What Is the Mark of the Beast in the Bible?" Christianity.com, April 25, 2021, https://www.christianity.com/wiki/end-times/what-is-the-mark-of-the-beast-in-the-bible.html.
4. Matthew 24:6 (NIV).
5. Matthew 24:7 (NIV).
6. John 3:16 (ESV).
7. John 3:5 (ESV).
8. John 14:6 (NIV).
9. Cody Carnes, vocalist, "Run to the Father" by Matt Maher, Ran Jackson, and Jay Cody Carnes, track 1 on *Run to the Father*, Sparrow Records, 2000.

## About The Author

Kim is a first-time author and wrote this novel after feeling compelled to write a fictional account of the last days based on Revelation. Her focus was to educate young adults on the possibilities that could occur in the first half of the seven-year tribulation. She felt a strong calling from God to write this book and feels that there is a need for young adults to hear the gospel in a way that they may be able to relate to better.

Kim currently lives in Sarasota, Florida. She has a bachelor's degree in nursing and is a certified psychiatric nurse. When Kim is not writing, she enjoys spending time with her family, traveling, and reading.

9 781685 561475